GW00647479

Seeking the Wisdom of the 50-year-old Woman

SARAH-ANNE LUCAS

Copyright © Sarah-Anne Lucas, 2020

Published by Known Publishing, 2020.

The right of Sarah-Anne Lucas to be identified as the
Author of her work has been asserted by her in accor-
dance with the Copyright, Designs and Patents Act 1988.

ISBN 978-1-913717-15-5

No part of this book may be reproduced by any mechan-
ical, photographic or electronic process, or in the form
of a phonographic recording, nor may it be stored in a
retrieval system, transmitted or otherwise be copied for
public or private use, other than for 'fair use' as brief
quotations embodied in articles and reviews, without
prior written permission of the author.

WWW.GET-KNOWN.CO.UK

> **"** *And if you've never felt your soul being torn apart, you've never loved anyone with all your heart.* **"**

REGINALDO KILAS

> "That's the thing about unhappiness, all it takes is for something worse to come along and you realise it was happiness after all."

AS SPOKEN BY THE CHARACTER OF QUEEN ELIZABETH II IN 'THE CROWN', SEASON 2

Preface

Sometimes it's not your job to fix it; it's your job to sit with them through their pain. The worst pain of all pains. The breaking of the heart.

Two years have passed since my vivacious daughter, Noos, found out that the love of the moment did not want her anymore. He had found "someone better". Her words of defeat made smoke rings in the air.

Take yourself back to being twenty-one, brimming with hope and promises from life. Then, one day, out of nowhere, "The One" you gave all to, punches his fist into your chest and tears out your heart, raising it high to the sun like a Viking claiming victory. Roaring that "She was not enough…"

As I watched the tears of shame and self-disgust trickle down her fresh face, she sobbed out her nightmares of what was to become of her.

"Who will want me now, Mumma?"

I swallowed her razor blade words whole, thinking them into my being. I felt my own pain again. The past endured the pain of heartbreak.

Sitting there listening to her torture me with her words of self-doubt, questioning what life and love are all about, I found myself wandering off into my own mind. I asked myself, "Does that matter to me now? Does what matters now to Noos in her twenties, matter to me now in my fifties?"

I cast my mind back to being her age, an animated twenty-year-old. How had I loved in my twenties? With complete abandonment of self. I definitely did not have the understanding of self-love, fulfilment or purpose back then. I only wanted to be loved by "The One". This truth shocked me. WTF… "Have a word with yourself… Bird!"

In my youth, I had loved with the absence of wisdom and the neglect of self. I had always believed that if he were happy and doing what he wanted then I would be happy too.

Only my future would show me how foolish those notions were.

I questioned whether the words of Noos were words of wisdom or just words of a woman desperate for the love of another. Someone to love her, to fulfil her Disney dreams of princess love.

Here's the first question of two, that I am seeking:

1. DOES WHAT MATTERED THEN MATTER NOW?

I searched for similarities, overlaying Noos' words onto mine. How different were they? Were they generations apart or were they the same words and feelings in different decades with nothing learnt but how to continue in cahoots with blind love?

As always, I then went deeper into my body, pondering whether I felt the same. I asked myself, "Did what matters to you now matter back then?"

Was I as jealous in my fifties as I was in my twenties? NO. I was once wild with jealously. I used to be like a hawk in the nightclubs, watching for my love to swoop onto the girls like prey as they wiggled and enticed him onto the dance floor. Come on, weren't you the same? Full of passion and sassiness… Now, I literally couldn't care less, I have seethed the jealousy right out of me.

And the second question I am seeking is:

2. HOW DO I FIND LOVE AGAIN?

Are you, like me, still wanting to make sense of tangible, unwavering true love?

That doesn't mean you have to be single looking for love. But still seeking love, wherever you are at or whomever you are with. Still seeking the wholeness of love... even with all the scars and battle wounds to show for it.

Or am I alone in this ever-decreasing circle of seeking?

I know I am not; you tell me every day. Women like you message me with their stories: stories of loss of love, affairs, loss of femininity, loss of feeling wanted, loss of feeling sensuous, loss of respect, loss of self and loss of love from their children who leave them feeling unappreciated or taken for granted.

Don't think these words are just from women, I am always stunned and paralysed when men share the same feelings, but with cockeyed perspectives.

Different words.

Different actions.

Different behaviours.

Imposter syndrome is the biggest murderer of masculinity.

I am blessed and cursed to see the whole of women, whose stories are inspiring, not just the pink, fluffy side but the raw, trueness of living and trying to love.

I want to know what you know, so I can aspiringly steal from you and reach levels of extraordinary only ever seen in the movies. You heard right, steal. I know that you, and all women, know the answers I am seeking.

"Why ohhh why are you still seeking the answers, Bird?" I hear you say... What is the question unanswered?

Because, my darling, I can't figure it out! It still doesn't make sense to me.

Love... How do I do it?

Family... It wasn't supposed to feel like this!

Success... What is that?

Money... Of course... lots more.

Life... What is it all about?

How do we find the courage AGAIN to trust in and hold onto love? That's a practice I have only found failure in.

That's where you come into the challenge of creating a picture out of all the pieces of wisdom you hold.

Ask women of all ages and decades: "How do We, you, I find love again?"

The birth of this book series

And so, it began, designing a space for truth-telling conversations. Modelling an interview technique by Ava Duvernay from her documentary *The Thirteenth* – if you want the truth, hold a conversation for a minimum of two hours and the truth will show its ugly head.

So that is exactly what I did.

I asked ten women, of each age decade (in their twenties, thirties, forties, fifties and sixties) the same twenty-one questions. At their heart, each of these 21 questions related to my 2 core questions.

The ten women in each decade were not in my circle of friends or business associates. I knew not to ask my women council. They were the worst to ask. They had been the nurses to my wounds. Far too close for truth.

I reached out far and wide to ask women to volunteer to share the wisdom they had gained through the stories of their lives.

Originally, I was just going to sit listen and take generalised notes. This very quickly proved unproductive. It needed open, guiding questions, focussed on what love meant to them.

I had expected to go back as the conversations evolved and ask different questions. Shockingly, the questions held the test of time and proved their worthiness to each decade. No need to adapt to age or appropriateness.

Like all beginnings, it never ends up where you predict. I was going to interview fifty women, collect the answers, look at trends, similarities of answers, wisdom shared, and then compare and contrast through the ages. I planned to write a compendium of all the findings. The thickest doorstop book of women's wisdom.

Do the maths, ten women of five decades in a two-hour interview adds up to hundreds of hours of interviews, let alone the analysis and wonderment. All before the writing process begins. I have the patience of Job, but I knew that the sheer volume would lose the essence of a dip-in and out philosophy.

One big bible of love was to be rejuvenated into five books, each handbag-worthy and super-fast to read. Short, sharp chapters that make you think, and more importantly make you curious to question self.

Each chapter begins with a question. The conversations always began with Question One; from there on, the women led the way. I merely felt the direction of the conversation and asked the questions in order of relevance as the conversations flowed, but not in numerical sequence.

I would encourage you to be brave and ask yourself each of the twenty-one questions too. That's where the magic happens. Ask yourself: what do I believe to be true, how would I answer that?

What you say and do are almost always different. So, when you ask yourselves these questions, I will hold you accountable to your words, listen and always follow you, hollering, "Now go do."

"Words are perspectives; actions are reality."

This book focusses on women in their fifty decade. Women, who I presumed would be saying farewell to their grown-up children and heading off naked into the sunset with independence as their new playmate. I have heard relentlessly from women that this decade is "their time". They have a new sense of freedom to pursue life on their terms with a wallet full of cash and a home not being owned by the bank or full of children.

Is this the decade, when you and I are going to be shown that empowered women are ready to press the reset button and take on the world in a crusade of finding their true self.

Or are these women going to present themselves as hormonally left wanting and financially unbalanced with dry, redundant vaginas?

Disclaimer...
Now hear this

Let's just talk about the amazing ten women who gave me two hours of their life to answer the twenty-one questions.

They were not given the questions in advance to prepare for the interview. In fact, "interview" really doesn't describe the beautiful, open conversations we had.

I did not see their faces, nor did I show mine. My facial expressions speak too much.

The questions were not forged to trick or lead. My intention was just to find out what these women knew.

Not to judge the words.

Not to guide or support them into an outcome I wanted to see and deliver to you.

Not to manipulate their words to give answers that align with my own beliefs.

I certainly did not want to end the book feeling like Miss Know-It-All.

Nor did I want to come to the end and say, "I told you so…".

With my hand on my heart, I can say with every cell in my being, I now have no idea who said what and when. The process and strategy of sifting the spoken words into trends created the needle in a haystack effect. Their identities were lost, so that only their words could be seen.

You will see their exact words in speech marks. Unnamed, without reference to an identity, a personality or a character, other than the quote given at the beginning of each chapter, e.g. Woman No.6.

Genius! I know, I just wished I could say it was pre-determined, but I styled it out.

Truly each woman, whomever you are… you are protected and anonymous.

Contents

Do You Know Who I Am? (she said in a very posh accent...)

Forgive me if we have met before, ignore this bit… and carry on. But if this is our first encounter, read on my darling…

My name is Sarah-Anne Lucas. All my friends and family call me "Bird", and I would love you to do the same.

What I do

I started out as a nurse, aged 24, but have since been a dance style aerobics instructor (I just loved the head mics – made me feel like Madonna), personal trainer and Pilates and movement teacher. More recently, I have become a businesswoman, setting up two companies in the Women's Empowerment space. I adore business, the jousting for position in the market, creating products of worth and adapting to stormy waters.

I am now a wannabe billionaire, the funniest International speaker, radio host/presenter/producer. I've been running a weekly show, *The Conversation*, for the last four years. It's a live one-hour radio show, where the guest and I openly show you their story. Can you imagine being in a coffee shop and overhearing the most inconceivable and captivating conversation? It's just like that. Without pretence, I share experiences with the most exceptional, elevated beings, all the while relating their story to yours. Poking you to ask yourself, "What do I believe to be true?"

Just in case you want to catch up with the any of the one hundred and fifty-nine shows, go to my website **BeautifulBraveBody.com** where all the shows and all the methods of listening to it are at your fingertips.

It is my favourite hour of the week. You see, I am curious about why you do what you do. Why you choose to rise, and others choose to remain? I want to know what you truly believe about success and love. What does it mean to you? What makes up the equation to your happiness?

I am sometimes teased for sounding like a pirate on my radio show because I come from the South-West of

England, where the days are slow, and people just pop in for a cup of tea without an invite. It is so beautifully friendly and welcoming (not full of pirates).

When I'm not writing or working, I'm a crazy Ironman athlete. I once got asked, "What are you training for...?" I replied: "Everything." Ironman training gives you a model for life. In fact, all training of your body gives you a model for life. You must believe in the plan, know that you will fail more than you will achieve, and it's not "will it hurt?" It's just when. You're consistently committed to the plan of enduring subjective pain. How much can you take and how will the outcome serve you?

Practising the art of practice. Some may call me an overachiever! (BTW... how can you overachieve?)

I have 3 extraordinary big people who are the reason I do what I do. You see, I take my role of being their mumma very seriously. I am their role model (alongside Kim Kardashian. I don't allow Kim the pure pleasure of inspiring them!)

Who I support

Women.

Women of all ages.

Women who want more from the life they find themselves in. They want more energy than their bodies can muster and want to look like they did when their skin didn't sag in places that it shouldn't.

Every day, literally every day, at least one woman will reach out and tell me about how they loath their thoughts, mind and their ugly, fat bodies. Hatred seeps into their words of body dysmorphia and being "not enough" to all who crowd their daily life.

When you hear these cries over and over, I dare you not to care. I care, and it has become a gift and a curse. Someone had to make a stand for women to stop this repeated script. Why not me? I took the baton handed to me, not by my ancestors but by my daughter. She tasered me into awakening my responsibility to her and you. I take what I do very seriously, nothing brings me greater joy than supporting women to be their children's inspiration. You and I dance with responsibility and duty to others but most importantly to self.

If there is one gift to share with you throughout

this book series, it is that you are not alone.

This is your story and mine.

There is a sisterhood out there, even though sometimes they disguise themselves as your worst critics! They know not what they do.

Throughout this series, you will learn who I am, my values and beliefs, my fears and areas that I need to heal. In seeing me, you will deeply want to see yourself.

I will always be brutally honest, never hiding the truth. It will set you free. What's the alternative to the truth, self-deception? That's just abuse poured upon yourself. You will never grow by lying. All that will happen is nothing will change, or worse, you will fade away and continue to be invisible.

Don't you worry, I will not let that happen...

Question 1

"Who are you
as a woman?"

"SOME WOMEN SAY I'M JUST ME...
I AM WHO I AM."

WOMAN NO.5

With trust blindly handed to me, the faceless, slightly nervous conversation began.

You may be asking why it was necessary for me to ask a gender-specific question. I could've asked "Who are you?" and not cared about the gender, but the question would've have been too open, rudderless.

I always like to start with a question that gives a deep, real answer. I like to call it "Poking the Bear". In fact, this question is one of the least probing questions. How could I understand women and their wisdom without understanding what being a woman looked like, felt like and meant to them?

Remember, I am the one on the discovery voyage, they are merely witnesses giving their evidence. With respect, being a woman is complex, and every woman has a different understanding of what being a woman means, unique to them.

Every question that I asked of these women, I also asked of myself. If I was asking them to be brave, open and honest, then I must be too. I have newly entered this decade and have wondered whether I still feel part of the previous decade, or whether I am actually aligned with this transformative decade. I feel more womanly now than I have ever felt. At this age, I am more aware of who I am and who I want to be defined as. Although I feel late to the table of business and purpose, as I didn't feel this power in my twenties or thirties. This energy is a new gift, freshly discovered and daily worked upon.

As they say, define me by my deeds.

The answers came thick and fast in this decade. Each woman showed zero hesitation to voice her understanding of what it meant to her to be a woman. The precision of

"I'm just me."

each woman's answer displayed a wisdom that is synonymous with this decade.

The answers

ROLES

Never in a million years did I think that in answering this question most of the women would define themselves by their roles: mother, wife, daughter, sister, friend and Mummy's girl.

BEHAVIOURS

Some women described their behaviours: energetic, hardworking, bored easily, independent, still curious, struggling with health but coping, happy, strong-willed, a good diffuser of family quarrels. Some said that they were unable to make decisions, which is so clichéd but common. They admitted to reaching out daily to friends for their permission on which way to go with a decision or "Calling Mum every day, needing confirmation on every decision, a simple OK… Just in case I get it wrong!"

COMPARISON

Interestingly, the verb "to compare" repeatedly bared itself. Who knew that my question would lead these women to compare themselves to their partners? It felt almost like a competition. Comparing wages or their position in the company. Who did the most work at home, shopping, cleaning or even spending time with the children?

MONEY

Money certainly came up with a globule of negativity, blindly voicing that it did not figure highly in their lives. Few believed it necessary or essential that they should seek financial independence.

CAREER

Few women described a career or job. Although one woman was looking for the holy grail: a job that gave her everything and children that loved her. She wanted to feel secure in being a woman.

And only one woman wanted a legacy based on what people would say about her: that "she helped lots of people". She never wanted to be accused of being selfish.

This gave me an image of her funeral; no, I am not being morbid. You know the scene, the beautiful fibs and accolades said about the dear departed. Her coffin laden with white lilies and people adoringly saying... her trophy words of success... "She helped lots of people."

Interestingly, this feeling of what others think and say takes centre-stage in later answers.

OTHERS

"Not sure what that question means," and she followed up these words with, "I don't know who I am as a woman..."

"I don't associate as a woman... I am a human being... I avoid women."

This gush of words came right at the end, just as we were talking our way into the next question.

Then without hesitation, one woman declared: "I'm just me..."

Bird's reflection upon the findings

What became evident was the exclusivity of womanhood to the individual. It is different for each of us.

The expectations of others add another layer of complexity to being a woman. The children's expectation of her is always there.

The partner's expectation of her to be here and be available, never absent. The internal pressure of making others' lives run smoothly and the attitude of society to "know your place, woman".

So, you see, you are not alone in your feelings, however you feel about being a woman. Trust what your body is saying to you. Listen intently with love and prepare to action the pathway your womanly spirit is taking you on.

Question 2

"What have you tolerated?"

And then...

"That you wouldn't tolerate now?"

"HE'S AN ARSE…
BUT HE'S MY ARSE."

WOMAN NO.2

I would be a millionaire by now if I had taken a pound for every time someone said to me, "You get what you tolerate!" Apparently so…! Silly me.

Is this the practicality of everlasting love, to tolerate?

"
Tolerating is
my nemesis.
"

In each interview, I waited with bated breath to see what these women's words would tell me to do, and the cost that we, as women, need to pay in the name of love.

Tolerating is my nemesis. It is my medal and my execution. It is, up until now, the single biggest barrier to life-long love for me. Why can't I leave "tolerating" behind? Is it just me? I wanted to ask other women about their experiences and see if I could unveil a positive side to the cross I bear. To understand what levels of toleration are necessary to win and raise the trophy of a long marriage.

You know by now that I like to "Poke the Bear", but before we begin to see the answers to this very loaded question, let's consider what "tolerate" truly means, the origin of the word.

The most basic meaning of the word "tolerate" is "to put up with or allow" (Oxford English Dictionary.com).

I am always intrigued by the deliberate practice of words. If we changed the word "tolerate" to "allow", "accept" or "compromise", it shifts our perception of the situation that we find ourselves in and changes the trajectory of our decision-making process.

The etymology, the origin of the word, changed everything for me.

The early fifteenth-century meaning of "Tolerate": "In the face of pain or hardship.[1]"

The early fourteenth-century meaning of "Tolerate": Old French. From Latin "tolerantia", "a bearing, supporting, endurance"[2].

I wanted to share the historical meaning of "tolerate" so that these women's beliefs you are about to read will make more sense.

The answers

These women's words fell into 5 main areas.

Only one way

Other people

Abuse

Infidelity

Finance

I'll be honest, although my objective was to be an

---

1 https://www.etymonline.com/

2 https://www.etymonline.com/

impartial listener throughout this project, I found this question the hardest to not judge (the answers, not the person).

In each interview, I was always in a gasp and agog at these women's answers. Left with my mouth wide open... I needed someone to come along and tell me to "close your mouth, dear."

Here's a list of some of the direct quotes. It is vital that you do not misinterpret their words through my eyes, only through your own. Breath in their words and sit with these women as I did. Do not rush through the pain of the truth they tell.

1. ONLY ONE WAY

When you read this section, 'Only One Way', what do you feel immediately as a result of these words? Don't judge yet! Listen to how these women harvest their love and realism.

"I loved in a different way then. I loved the person so much that his way was the only way."

"With new friends, seeing new lives, the belief in myself grew. I do not normalise bad behaviour now."

"He never listens to me, not wanting to hear my truth. Other's opinions override mine."

"Making and keeping the peace to keep everything running smoothly… It's a woman thing, you know."

"Women look at the consequences, they look at the bigger picture."

"My husband can be really unpleasant, but I ignore it. The behaviour doesn't register with me."

I loved their acknowledgement, realism and the practicalities they put in place back then and now.

2. OTHER PEOPLE

In this fifty decade, not valuing or caring what others think becomes abundantly important to each woman. Yes sister, no more!

"I used to do what everyone else wanted me to do… Allowing people into my space when I didn't want to do that."

"I was a magnet for people having no regard for time or space… Now I do not tolerate people who waste my time."

"I tolerated how people spoke to me… Not anymore. I tolerated people's opinions; now I have zero tolerance as it affects my wellbeing. I do not tolerate disloyalty in a friendship anymore, I have grown up."

And there it is, the ongoing growth of caring less about what people think.

3. ABUSE...

I was surprised to learn, specifically in this fifty decade, that two out of the ten women tolerated physical, mental and emotional abuse. I am not surprised about abuse being present in relationships. Merely that they chose to stay when I chose to leave. Neither right nor wrong, just personal.

"The fear of losing him and the infrequency of the action allowed me to tolerate."

I get it. Paralysed by the fear of loss.

We, as humans, always choose the lesser of two pains. The feeling of knowing how to behave in an unsafe environment with the person you fell in love with is a lesser pain than leaving the known, to go to a greater pain, the unknown loneliness.

4. INFIDELITY

At one point in ALL but one of the ten women's relationships, one partner had been a philanderer. Interestingly, only one woman out of the nine was the one who sought another love. This is not reflective of recent 2018 studies.

The Institute for Family Studies (IFS) and The General Social Survey (GSS) have been collating infidelity rates for decades. Generally speaking, men are more likely to cheat than women. Although the GSS data finds the rate of women cheating has increased over the twenty years by forty per cent, particularly in middle age.

"A marriage that should've ended, a long time ago. But I wanted to keep my family together. I know it would've been braver to walk away. It was a trade-off, for the family, and it worked."

"It's the relationship I find myself in... Minimal intimacy or sex."

Not only had each woman been touched by treachery but so had their close friends. It seemed that this was a normal occurrence, yet an unexpected act of betrayal and one that was worked through with the outcome that they stayed married. Each woman believed she had worked for too long and hard to lose her man to "the other" woman!

I hear you, and I so get it.

5. FINANCE

Nine out of the ten women spoke of money being the contributing factor to what they tolerated within their relationship.

"I tolerated things, bad behaviour for fear of having no money. I had to put up with things because we needed the money."

"The financial hardship post leaving the relationship and seeking the divorce made me stay for too long. The inevitable happened anyway."

Never did I see this coming from this decade, a lack of finances being the reason to stay. It is not the only reason. Change never occurs from just one factor, but the sum of many factors. You will see this become more visible in the women's words to follow.

Bird's reflection upon the findings

I am honoured to hear the truth and shocked to believe that we, you and I, still tolerate bad behaviour in the name of love and marriage. Bugger!

Yet, I know to my core that you and I are doing our very best, even with the dread of getting older and being left on the shelf and being paralysed by loss. Although it seems we have passed the repeated script of "Who will want me now?" down to our young women. I can still hear my daughter, "Noos" weeping the words into being.

What work do we still have to do to change this dichotomy of woman? The juggling, while balancing act of loving and tolerating.

We must do the work of "Show me, don't tell me." This is a daily practice I am consistently doing the work on. May my lips oil my joints to create action.

We must practice the hard, right behaviour – actually doing it rather than just speaking about it. We, as women, are still not where women in the nineteenth century could see we needed to be. We have work to do.

Sojourner Truth is still as relevant today as her words were in 1851. I want to share with you her speech: *Ain't I A Woman?*

Sojourner Truth (1797-1883): Ain't I A Woman?

DELIVERED 1851

WOMEN'S RIGHTS CONVENTION,
OLD STONE CHURCH (SINCE DEMOLISHED),
AKRON, OHIO

Well, children, where there is so much racket there must be something out of kilter. I think that 'twixt the negroes of the South and the women at the North, all talking about rights, the white men will be in a fix pretty soon. But what's all this here talking about?

That man over there says that women need to be helped into carriages, and lifted over ditches, and to have the best place every-where. Nobody ever helps me into carriages, or over mud-pud-dles, or gives me any best place! And ain't I a woman? Look at me! Look at my arm! I have ploughed and planted, and gathered into barns, and no man could head me! And ain't I a woman? I could work as much and eat as much as a man – when I could get it – and bear the lash as well! And ain't I a woman? I have borne thirteen children, and seen most all sold off to slavery, and when I cried out with my mother's grief, none but Jesus heard me! And ain't I a woman?

Then they talk about this thing in the head; what's this they call it? [member of audience whispers, "intellect"] That's it, honey. What's that got to do with women's rights or negroes' rights? If my cup won't hold but a pint, and yours holds a quart, wouldn't you be mean not to let me have my little half measure full? Then that little man in black there, he says women can't have as much rights as men, 'cause Christ wasn't a woman! Where did your Christ come from? Where did your Christ come from? From God and a woman! Man had nothing to do with Him.

If the first woman God ever made was strong enough to turn the world upside down all alone, these women together ought to be able to turn it back and get it right side up again! And now they is asking to do it, the men better let them.

Obliged to you for hearing me, and now old Sojourner ain't got nothing more to say.

Question 3

"What stimulates you now?"

"HOW THE WORLD HAS CHANGED… INTER-
ACTIONS WITH PEOPLE… RELATIONSHIPS.
I WANT TO BE IN TOUCH WITH HOW THEY
THINK…"

WOMAN NO.7

During the hour of my weekly radio show, I'm always intrigued to find out what drives people. Is that driver the difference between being hungry for purpose or accepting contentment. What stimulates you to want more than the life you find yourself lost in? That's what fascinates me.

The lost and the lonely, the blamers and the victims, the sad and the "why me" brigade. I have been and walked with all those characters, thankfully not all at the same time. Can you imagine being around me in my darkest hours? Not a bundle of laughs, and I have a very ugly cry.

All these extreme characters have a missing link in that moment: a stimulation. I'm talking about:

- *A fire in the belly that will not be dampened out*

- *A hunger that brings a metal taste to your saliva*

- *Something that excites you, but really incites you more.*

Without that stimulation, we can all become lost, and that, my darling, is where the crisis brews.

Thank goodness for knowing the wisdom of gently cupping stimulation. My Nan modelled this with every cell in her body... consistently.

My Nan had the most beautiful, sculpted arms at the age of eighty-four. Yes, you heard right, eighty-four. No bingo wings there. I have her photo on my son's piano, standing behind my seated grandad, hands placed upon his shoulders. Her body displaying the evidence of her daily stimulation. Keep Fit.

She was in the National Keep Fit team until she was eighty-five. Although her love of movement and belonging to a community began in the early 1950s. She was smack-bang at the beginning age of women's empowerment.

Because my nose was rubbed into this ideology, I can never remember a time of not knowing.

Here's where it gets exciting.

YOU know this too. You who are in your fifth decade. It is your duty to continue to seek wonderment, to find reason in what you do and adapt your focus to who you are becoming.

Now, here is where my teeth come out… (a teeth out moment is when you get excited). This usually happens when I am going *zoom* on my bike or snowboard.

The answers

Not one interviewee vented a lack of purpose. In fact, they too, like Nan, lived daily with the wisdom of finding stimulation in something.

Never did I believe the answers would be found in the simple things of life. They were:

1. *Self*
2. *Family*
3. *Others*

"We have been bred to be at the bottom of the pile.

1. SELF

Reaching fifty, with hormonal change as a bedfellow, has injected consistent routines into three women's days. Being proactive in the crusade against the cliché menopausal views.

"To achieve goals both personal and professional."

All of the women gently slipped into the conversation the need to prioritise goals for themselves and create bucket lists to direct and fulfil their want for more. They were unable to define what "more" looked like, just more than what they were, or even where they found themselves to be in life.

More didn't have to be complicated, it was simply to go out socialising guilt-free. The love of travel was, at last, being reignited by the returning freedom that was once stolen by having children.

An overwhelming need to connect to self, thundered through each answer.

2. FAMILY

Three women were aware of how their family dynamics had grown up from being a shared parental dictatorship to a children-parent democracy. This control shift had happened vigorously but without the lift of the burden of finances. Basically, the children of the household wanted to be unsupervised but financially dependent!

"I want to stay in touch with how they think."

One woman wanted to stay in touch with the next generation. To fully understand how her children thought, especially how they loved their new partners, now they were in their late twenties. She understood the essential need to love and accept her own child's new partner "No Matter What!"

"To keeping loving my children and their partners."

This opened up a new conversation for me with each of these insightful women. A discovery conversation of loving your child and their chosen life, regardless of your own perceptions or opinions.

3. OTHERS

I was pleased to see that "others" came last in this question. About time, ladies!

If ever there is a guilt felt by mothers, it is the guilt of putting themselves first. I get it, we have been bred to be at the bottom of the pile, to feed everyone else and eat last. Please, no more!

"I love talking to people, hearing their stories."

This bewilderment of human behaviour had not always been an area of interest to some of the women. Now they felt it vital to understand their environment. Observing how the world has changed and wanting to be a part of it.

"I have the extremes of behaviour."

This woman did not see it necessary or even an option to adapt herself. She sought out "her people" who would understand and accept her, just the way she was.

Perhaps this outward seeking stance would reflect a sense of balance within. This also showed up in more than half of the conversations, a willingness to learn and increase knowledge.

Bird's reflection upon the findings

This decade feels to me one of humongous change. Not just in terms of circumstances but also each woman's body. Can you imagine the rush and simultaneous depletion of hormones racing in and out of every cell? No wonder extreme behaviour was felt within.

I am super excited that these women know the

importance of stimulation. And the fact that they put themselves first, is even more exciting. Probably for the first time ever!

These women have created an optimism I have not felt in a very long time. A champagne bubble of positivity. This decade is an exciting one to behold.

To my astonishment, simplifying the complexity of life was the greatest stimulation.

Who knew?

Question 4

"What matters now... that didn't matter then?"

I introduced you to the story, a true-life story of Noos, my daughter, being dumped by a boy. Let's call him a boy, even though his years would be indicative of a man. Still makes me snarl, so a boy he shall be named.

"What matters now… that didn't matter then?" or "What mattered then… that doesn't matter now?"

This was the question that my weird thoughts created, then and there, not, "Is she OK?" This is what I was thinking when I should have been trying to soothe my daughter, telling her, "It's going to be OK…There's plenty more fish in the sea."

I know… shame on me… No dear friend, you and I know, no words can take away the pain.

This question is the reason you and I are here today. Are you, like me, still asking and needing love to be the answer? Was the pain worth it? Did I truly love, with every inch of me? How do I find love, true love again, after all the hurt and covered-up scars?

The answers to this question didn't even touch on love. Have the women transformed into realists and left romance for the young and inexperienced? What do you hear from their words?

The answers

Every time I asked this question an uncontrollable potty-mouthed woman appeared. They would shout me down immediately with a certainty of never going back to who they once were. Venom dripped out of each experience of love lost. These women were intent on never returning to love, unless on their own terms. Their desire for answers proved to me they had learnt their lesson, that life was so much more than just what had mattered back then.

The answers fell into two inter-related groups:

"

Personal
confidence
mattered now.

"

1. *Health*

2. *Lifestyle*

1. HEALTH

Health matters now, but didn't matter back then. I wonder why? (Sarcasm, much!)

Youth gave our bodies an invisible cloak, just like in *Harry Potter*. The years became skilled like a magician and made The Cloak of Youth bloody disappear. It seems these women didn't see health as a necessary commodity back then. Or could it be that the factors they used to define health were not related to energy or lack of movement because the symptoms were lying dormant, waiting for time to call on their presence?

So now, as if by magic, in their fifties, they can see that health is vital to their bodies.

Health comes in all guises. Energy, having a zest for life. Not waking up in the morning feeling like a "fat carcase rolling out of bed." (Her words, definitely not mine.)

"Health matters more now. It is the ability to adapt." Why does it matter more now? I would love it to have mattered to these women back then.

It is constantly repeated throughout most of these interviews that adapting is a necessary skill for this decade.

"Giving up drinking, helped. Got me back to basics."

Alcohol was an absent friend to some of these women. Although on the other end of the seesaw, alcohol was a refinement to their new privilege of being a socialite. Not one woman stood in the middle of the seesaw, balancing.

2. LIFESTYLE

Health and lifestyle changes became identical twins within the answers.

Now, lifestyle changes entwined themselves with a change in the way that love was seen – not needing materialistic things and how the friend selection process differed.

Interestingly, for some reason, being attached to things in their twenties permitted acceptance from "friends!" Now, they are able to let go of people's acceptance, "Things don't mean much now."

"No need to escape, holidays, buying things, spending too much time on going out. I had no idea who I was. So, I numbed in shopping, ran from being present with myself and didn't know how to say NO."

The opinions of others now mattered less than back then. The care of what people thought and said shifted from when they were younger.

This shift in thinking leaked into partnership relationships.

Personal confidence mattered now. However, four women sought confidence in how much they were loved by their partners, and in how their partners supported and tolerated their insecurities. One woman saw how much her partner loved her as being a cure to how little confidence she'd held as a younger woman. His love had balanced out her lack of self-confidence and enabled her to develop that side of herself.

Now, the word "responsibility" repeated itself throughout all of the ten interviews. They felt it was their responsibility to love themselves. Apologies, I mean to begin to like themselves. Their starting point was too far removed. To go straight into loving oneself would be an impossible quest. If you have never run before and I ask you to go and run 5 marathons back to back; quite rightly you would say it was impossible.

Perfect example of this.

Life timeline matters now. Three women described their mortality, their respect for precious time left and the need not to waste it.

"When you are young, you have loads of years ahead, now I seem to take life a lot more seriously."

"I value life now, I larked about when I was young."

In each conversation, there was a moment of "There she is!" A knowing, connected glint shared and smiled with the self and then with me. I see her, you, I, in our glorious femininity. Provocative femininity.

Bird's reflection upon the findings

Shocked and stunned is an apt description of how I felt when I did not hear from these ten women that love was a contributing factor to what matters now. How can that be?

Although love of one's health and wellbeing was spoken of in every conversation.

The self-confidence levels of each woman mattered more now. It is impressive that they were all now skilled at DIY self-love. No more searching for validation in others.

Have you noticed the repetition of behaving in the extremities? In the last chapter, one woman acknowledged this beautifully. Is this the decade of seeking balance?

The balance of self, purpose and love.

Your life is your responsibility, so don't waste time blaming others for how you feel and what you don't have or haven't done with your life.

Go do the work of seeking the answer to the most "drop the mic" question that I asked the women: "What do you want?"

Question 5

"What are your values and beliefs?"

"REALLY SIMPLE… ALWAYS SPEAK THE TRUTH… WITH ANYTHING AND EVERYTHING."

WOMAN NO.3

In asking this question, I was asking the collective ten to speak to the lone woman, me. I needed answers. What do I have to do and be to have enduring love? What values and beliefs form the foundation for lasting love? I hope you can feel me grappling and searching for the secret techniques, fool-proof strategies and limitless boundaries that I was not privy to at school. If only they had taught such lessons!

> **Values and beliefs are boundaries. They create the shape of you.**

Did I not hold the right values and beliefs to be successful in a loving, respectful relationship?

And there it is, the full disclosure of my most important value. The one word that echoes in every relationship I hold, be it romantic, family, friend, business or anyone come to that: RESPECT.

Values and beliefs are boundaries. They create the shape of you. I wanted to hear and see the shape of these women, their lived boundaries and life frameworks.

Seven of the ten women were in long-term marriages, the three remaining were divorced. I did not actively seek out this ratio; it's mere coincidence.

The answers

With minimal hesitation, the answers hurried from the knowing lips of each woman. All explained how their values and beliefs have had a miraculous makeover on the way they live their lives with the added factor of time.

Each woman knew that her values and beliefs had been sculpted from her own unique experiences, not just those that had been inherited from her female ancestors. So, it's really interesting that, despite their very different lives, their answers all fell into three main categories.

1. *Self*
2. *Family and friends*
3. *Others*

The three categories somehow gooed into each other. And yes, goo is a word in the dictionary, and you can use it in Scrabble. The past tense of goo is gooed. Within these three categories came unapologetic actions and wordy principles.

1. SELF

This one sentence says it all:

"I am doing the best that I can. Although, internally, I say, "I could've been a better mother. Even though I was doing the best that I could'."

I believe they call this an emotional sandwich. First, you start with a slice of positivity, then spread the filling of harsh sour truth and finally, place the last slice on the top of the sandwich with zeal. Tah-dah, one homemade emotional sandwich. This is the first time I have seen it applied on self.

Trusting that someone is doing their best right at this moment, that they can give no more, is the most beautiful, compassionate gift to hand to another woman. It's not an easy practice, and I often forget to action it, but when I do, it gives to both me and you.

"Have your head up, rather than down."

The way you carry your body matters. It makes a difference to how you feel, what you look like and it gives your energy levels a boost.

"Work is good for you."

I have always been surrounded by hard-working men and women. I have seen how it forces you to keep moving forward and never give up.

"Go to sleep knowing you have done a good job."

These women absolutely valued working. Having a purpose, being needed, knowing that what they do is valued and matters to people. Working links back to something that came up in Question 1 – how important it is for you and I to have a sense of financial independence? For me, that is the biggest driver to women's empowerment, making independent decisions with regard to money.

"Always surround myself with experienced people, my kind of people."

"I take a lot of responsibility for others, sometimes taking on their responsibilities."

When I heard this sentence, I must have looked like a woman possessed, screaming: "Yes, that's me!" Do you feel the same when you hear her wisdom?

"Really simple, always speak the truth with everyone about anything."

I totally agree but it needs a loving, respectful intention to be stained into the truth told. Come to people with a sense of care, wanting them to build, not break from your words.

One word was repeated, duplicated and echoed within every two-hour interview: kindness.

"I believe in kindness, no matter what."

"Just be kind, always kind and help others."

"Kindness and compassion, staying compassionate is a must."

Of course, be kind. What a delicious and elegant souvenir to take away from the two hours spent with each woman.

Bird's reflection upon the findings

At this moment of seeking, I have not found in this question what I was looking for. I asked this question to understand my failings within my belief system and my own values, to hear from these women what I needed to do and then action what was working for them. WRONG!

I admired these women's total immersion in the practice of actioning their values and beliefs. Never did I predict that kindness would be emphasised as being of value. Hearing those words created one of those obvious, enchanted moments.

An aligned woman began to expose her self-confidence, her innate energy and her feminine power.

These women were at the height of their awareness, brave in their action, and brazenly standing tall.

Question 6

"What does love look like to you?"

"MILK IN THE FRIDGE AT ELEVEN
O'CLOCK AT NIGHT."

WOMAN NO.10

Woman number ten, you are so right. That's exactly what love looks like to me, now! That somebody thinks of you above and beyond their needs, sometimes.

Or, as another woman said, "It's the small kindnesses that nobody else sees, or knows."

It matters what you believe love to look like to you. If you don't know, how can you sieve out the wheat from the chaff? It matters what you value in love. It matters what love looks like now. Being in the present with what you believe "to love" is. If I was looking for love, I would need a deeper understanding of what these different women understood about what I sought: love. How you want to love and be loved is important, but equally important is how the person you have chosen to love wants to be loved.

The answers

It was fascinating how the previous question prompted fluid answers, but this question prompted a frigidity that caught me off-guard. I expected easy answering, not pregnant pauses and stuttering. Do I stand alone, is this question hard? What do you think?

Were these women lazy in love? Did they just stay in their local stomping ground and wait to be attractive to someone or was love the unconscious working in alignment with the Eros, The Greek God of Love and Sex?

These aligned women described love in relation to three prefixes.

4. *I (self)*

5. *They (their beloved)*

6. *Them (their family and friends)*

" Love is clean
and cosy. "

1. I

Here are some examples of 'I' love. Do not confuse my chuckles with mockery, but these ladies made me laugh.

"Love is clean and cosy."

Love, to me, has never been clean and cosy. Have you seen how they use the toilet, and don't get me started on the noises and mess of sexy time?

"It's a feeling, a feeling of warmth, a connection, feeling secure and glowing."

"The sun coming up in the morning."

To me, there is nothing better than watching the sun pop up, that breath that you take is pure love.

This security of loving and being loved categorically, no matter what, did not matter so much to me when I was younger, but it so much matters now. This I know for sure will not be the answers of the women I will interview in their twenties. This has come from loving, losing and finding love again. The mere act of being loved as I wanted to be in my twenties is not enough now, I want simplicity! Simplicity is only ever birthed from suffering and the complexities of being misunderstood. Sit with these words. Breathe them into the belly of your pelvis, relax your shoulders and then wiggle your jawline from side to side, smile. And there you are!

Don't move on yet, stay here in this moment a while. When you have seen YOU, smile, then release and off you go.

2. THEY

Then comes their love for their beloved.

I was led into a closed debate of who loves who the most. One woman said she had equal love, "He loves me as much as I love him."

Another woman, unbiasedly shared, "You can't love in the same way. Love is empowered to self."

Two women described their men as positive and steady, "He's a good man," and "He's my rock."

And three women with nigh-on identical stories said that if they asked him to do a little job, it might get done. But if they asked him to do the almost impossible, he always delivered. I call this Your Shite in Khining Farmour… (Knight in Shining Armour)

Do you not do this, change the letters around to make the smarmiest aphorism relevant. You don't want to agree, but you do secretly. It's just funny!

3. THEM

One of the women said that supporting family dynamics is love. I am bereft of this love. How many times have you gone to the fridge to get "your food" and the buggers have eaten it? You can laugh, but no matter what else is in the fridge, your food tastes the best. I am positive that it is premeditated. They see it going in there, and eye it up for when I am not looking. Well, sister, this is not love, it's theft.

"Watching the love between children, siblings, that's love."

"Love to me is reaching out to others with open hands."

"Love looks like total happiness. To not be struggling with jealousy or lack of confidence."

"Love is harmony."

These women make loving your family look easy. For me, the children will come and go, they will need you, your money and then freedom. But the love is there, cellularly. Love to another, giving it away unprotected is so much more demanding on self.

Bird's reflection upon the findings

I applaud the courage, the grace and dignity that I have witnessed within these ten conversations. You see, I was never looking for my vision to be echoed in what these women thought of love. I wanted to know where I got it so wrong and rectify my mistaken movie of love. I wanted to hear the facts, listen and see her.

The love these women feel today is a personal love, which has been developed from within, not from how they have been loved. An empowered love. Super potent.

How our eyes saw love back then is definitely not the same as how our eyes look at love now. They see love now with a hesitant courage and a stale, bloodshot distortion, with the antidote to the historical vulnerably, being the constancy and security of the relationship.

> **"**
>
> *You cannot grow where money does not flow.*
>
> **"**

"What is the key to empowerment?"

"EMPOWERMENT IS FREEDOM..."

WOMAN NO.1

By now, you will probably have noticed that each of the twenty-one questions are deep, meaningful questions. Not superficial, pretty questions. But ones that show you the adventure of the thoughts and feelings of each woman.

We all know what empowerment is, what my prying thoughts wanted to know was how do you and I open the lock to this on-trend word. What do we all have to do to truly be or feel empowered? That is what I sought to find out from these women.

A whole business genre has been created around women's empowerment, one in which I work in, so now we have no excuse not to be empowered. But how do we actually do it?

The answers

I wish you could've been a fly on the wall in the interviews. It was a truly awakening experience. I held a space for every spoken word and consciously ignored my own beliefs.

Prepare to have your emotions go up and down like a whore's drawers. You may even throw this book across the room, if you dare!

Interestingly, the answers fell around 3 topics:

1. *Self-belief*
2. *Money*
3. *Freedom to choose*

1. SELF-BELIEF

Each of these direct words from the ten women came with an absolute laissez-faire response. When I hear and read these words, they fill me with pride for my fellow women.

"Self-belief is the key."

"A mind less cluttered a

"Consciousness, confid the key."

"Knowing who you ar Giving my opinions has on

2. MONEY

Whenever I speak of teous side steps up. I was s woman believe in the pow in my thoughts.

"It's about the mon Money gives you choices."

This was the only wo in answer to this questi stunned to hear that lack tive in loveless marriages. deemed an important cor This is a fashion followed If there is one movemer into, it is women's wealtl radical difference upon y to create financial indeper

velopment. Money is a vital ingredient to creating the life you find growth in. You cannot grow where money does not flow.

3. FREEDOM TO CHOOSE

The word empowerment brought the vivaciousness out of some women. What is it about the word "freedom" that gives a sense of vast space to our inner being?

The word "freedom" makes you take in a long nasal, even tempo, deep involuntary breath.

"Empowerment is freedom and freedom comes with responsibility. When you are clear on your role with responsibility, then you can handle anything."

The word "choices" was also parroted throughout each interview.

"Understand you have choices. Accepting that we have the ability to have choices is the key."

Maybe it is not control or power that women are seeking but freedom to be. Nothing more. The essence of a woman is to hold freedom into her breasts with chutzpah.

Bird's reflection upon the findings

I felt held by these women's answers. Elevated to a higher self. It brought an energy that radiated from me like a nuclear power station.

Thank you, beautiful women, for holding me up and elevating my potential ability by showing me this. True role modelling. Without asking or expecting me to follow but to build a clear and precise pathway for me to begin to take daily steps.

From these words of wisdom came this equation: Money creates choices, empowerment is freedom and freedom comes with responsibility. Responsibility brings self-accountability, which creates a direct force to make decisions.

Now go do: Begin the art and practice of making empowered decisions.

Question 8

"Do you have a voice? And who gave it to you?"

"YES... I GAVE IT TO MYSELF..."

WOMAN NO. 6

Just like comedy, equality is all about the timing.

Timing of knowing.

Timing of allowing.

Timing of using.

Here in the UK, there are minimal restrictions (if any) on women having a voice within their communities. Unlike some parts of the globe, where a woman's

> **I have always had a voice; I gave it to myself.**

voice is forbidden, and women are not seen let alone heard.

History has provided me and you in the UK with the greatest chance of equality. Never have women been given a greater piece of the pie as they've been granted today.

Despite all of this, I still hear every day, and I mean *every* day, the distress of women who do not feel like they are seen or heard. I feel I have been passive for far too long, so I wanted to ask a question to get to the heart of the matter. Do women believe they have a voice? If so, how can we entice women to speak heavily with certainty, pushing themselves forward?

Why is it that the women of our history took action to pave the way for future generations, only for their hard-won currency not to be used? Visualise an old Victorian woman lying on her death bed, taking her last breath as she comes to realise that her life savings, safely hidden underneath her mattress, were wasted. She slowly dies knowing what riches she could've touched. She had saved in silence rather than investing in living loudly. That's you with your voice, hidden safely away, fearful to spend it just in case!

Currency can be anything. We know currency to be money. But your voice is your currency. Currency is a commodity that we swap chickens for. I call it swapping chickens. I have a skill; you have a skill, let's swap rather than cross each other's hand with silver.

The answers

The women felt that either:

1. *They had always had a voice*
2. *Time had given them a voice*

1. THEY HAD ALWAYS HAD A VOICE

Super interestingly, this decade showed that only two women knew, from the beginning of their time, they had a voice.

"I do have a voice; my parents gave it to me."

"The lovely upbringing my parents provided gave me the ability to express myself."

The other of the two punched me in the face with her words. "I have always had a voice; I gave it to myself."

2. TIME

The majority of the women felt that time gifted them their voice.

"Now, time is running out and some things just have to be said. Hear me, I am important."

"Yes, I do now. A couple of years ago I didn't want to upset people."

People have a lot to answer for! The care for other's opinions is an excuse rinsed and repeated as to why women have silently suffered and not embarked on many of life's challenging quests. Just stop. Stop pathetically caring about unenlightened souls. They know not what they do.

"Everybody has a voice, but you have to connect with it."

"I didn't get taken seriously years ago because of my actions. The words to follow had no meaning. But gradually it happened through my forties."

Few had not seen their voice at all until fear raised its ugly head and unnaturally manipulated them to speak.

"Fear made me find a voice. I was powerless in the face of splitting with my husband, I had no profession and no qualifications."

The same twisted romanticism but slightly different: "I didn't have a voice when I was younger, I had a fear of losing him if I spoke my will."

"I do now, post leaving my marriage. I gave me the voice. How? Belief in self. Knowing that I don't want this anymore."

Sometimes electrifying pain forces the imprisoned voice to involuntarily roar. There is no putting the lid on that marvellous voice now, it remains wildly free.

Bird's reflection upon the findings

My first big shock from the interviews was the discovery that we, you and I, are still not as free as I (and maybe you) thought we were.

Who knew that more of us were bereft of a voice than those who have acknowledged and allowed themselves the choice to speak?

Running out of time, no longer being prevented by not wanting to upset people and deciding who has the power pushed these women to find their voice and scream as they fell off the cliff into the abyss. Without knowing if they would survive, let alone whether they would fly. Flying nor surviving was never the outcome; they just wanted the pain to stop.

It is obvious to all that we have a voice. What most of us have abandoned is our right to choose the skill of voice. It is your duty to be brave and practise giving sound to your words. Think your words into being, write them down and then speak them aloud to an audience of one, YOU. I do not know any great speaker that does not write down their words first, practice to themselves, then and only then do they share their thoughts with others. Practice writing first, then speak afterwards.

Question 9

What creates your self-belief and your confidence?

"MONEY, EVERY WOMAN SHOULD HAVE AN INCOME THAT THEY HAVE CONTROL OVER."

WOMAN NO. 4

With each question, the interview excavated more from each woman with trends repeating themselves. Duplications of behaviour become visible over the intensity of time. These behaviours cannot hide themselves from the lies of the truth that we tell ourselves.

It was vital I got out of my own way with this question and open up to receive the spoken wisdom. To me, it is ridiculously obvious. Forgive me if you mistake my

Confidence is a task-orientated skill.

knowing for arrogance. The action must come before the feeling. You cannot cheat the process of confidence. The confidence process is simple, you must action first, complete the task, regardless of the outcome of failure or success. In fact, you only build confidence by both failing and succeeding in the task. Confidence is a task-orientated skill.

However, I was curious as to how each woman found their self-belief and confidence, perhaps I could find a method less scary and intimidating than the only confidence process I know.

The answers

The answers poured from these women, and I was touched that they all felt were responsible for their own self-belief.

Here are the three golden trends that came through in this question and interestingly, are also repeated in most of the women's answers to all of the questions so far:

1. *Self*

2. *Others*

3. *Environment*

Others and Environment are bunkbed mates and therefore share the same room. Where one goes the other surely follows, unlike previous questions where others and environment have had their own entries. I was unable to decipher these – they were a single entity, they were interlinked and entwined.

1. SELF

They all instinctively knew that confidence starts with self. It is not about asking for the support of others or blaming the environment that they chose to place themselves in. It came from within.

"Learning to accept yourself."

"Accepting the knowledge I have."

"Knowing I am made for a purpose; it's up to me to find it so I can have an abundant life."

"I create the place for me to be. I have created the model without realising it."

"Taking my career into a different pathway, it changed my personality. I grew into me; I grew into my personality."

"Getting fit, grew me."

"I take great pride in my looks, that I smell nice. Looking your best builds confidence."

2. OTHERS AND ENVIRONMENT

I wonder if "They" know how much they are to blame for building or breaking the spirit of a woman. Or is it our responsibility to surround ourselves with delicious people?

"Being around the right people."

"Continual reinforcement as a child. Unpractical beliefs with no limitations. I was told you can do anything you want."

"I create the place for me to be. I have created a model without realising it. I can run the business anywhere in the world."

This decade of women certainly gifted me a feeling of acceptance. When you reach this stage in your life and are a certain age: "It all falls into place, as it is. Happy."

Bird's reflection upon the findings

These retorts liberated me. These women prov-ed me wrong. It seemed I did not need to get out of the way of the answers, each woman sailed me away with their understanding of owning their self-belief, their confidence.

Confidence only appears from doing.

The doing comes first, the feeling of confidence comes second. It may take time, maybe more time than you had hoped for. Nevertheless, in time, you will appear triumphant in grace.

The magic of grace. Possessing the power to transform an instant into something greater.

This one answer immediately rehabilitated my business approach. It was shared at the time of asking this question. It does not fit into one of the categories, it deserves a room of its own. I will gift it to you with the same love as it was gifted to me, as it was gifted to her from her mother...

"Whatever you want, go to the top."

It doesn't get more practical than that.

Question 10

"What is expected of you?"

"DINNER AT THE TABLE FOR
SEVEN-THIRTY AT NIGHT."

WOMAN NO. 8

There's another shocker of an answer, but maybe not to you. Now is not the time for me to stand on my soapbox, spouting my feminist courteous contemplations at you. Now is the time for me to listen to these women and seek their wisdom, no matter what that wisdom is. If that sounds judgemental, forgive me; sincerely, there is no judgement being handed out.

I loved hearing that one woman felt that it was expected from her family, led heavily by her husband, to

> **"Women clench onto others' expectations like world-class rock climbers."**

have dinner on the table at seven-thirty. My nan whole-heartedly believed this to be her duty to her family. She would be triumphantly and gleefully swinging from the rafters at this old-fashioned action. She and many of her generation believed this was the way to a man's heart. I wish I could disagree, but even me, The Ardent Feminist, believes and agrees to "feed love" to her family. I get it. I can feel the eggs of shame being thrown at me from you, you angry vaginas.

I asked this question because I can't remember a time when my children or partner didn't expect me to do or be something, everything. I really have tried to fulfil every whim, but have I lost some of my self-worth in the process? I wanted to find out how other women balance this juggling act.

It seems that we, women, clench onto others' expectations like world-class rock climbers. With our fingertips barely holding onto the edge of a cliff, one false move and death awaits us. A bit dramatic, but tell me I am wrong.

The answers

The answers, unsurprisingly, fell largely into the two groups I had most keenly felt in my life:

1. *Partner's expectations*
2. *Family's expectations*

Oh, and somewhere right at the end of it all, self-expectation was the executioner to self-fulfilment.

1. PARTNER'S EXPECTATIONS

Interestingly, these expectations were not all burdensome. The expectations of some men were hugely positive, with nothing but adoration for their partner.

"He wants me to be healthy and to enjoy life. To have a content life with my children and grandchildren."

Although not strictly part of the question, a couple of women volunteered their own expectations of their partners:

One woman told me she expects her partner "to be truthful, to show up and be reliable". This is what she gives to him; therefore, it is only right and proper for him to return the favour.

A beautiful twist came from another woman, who

had no expectations of her husband at all.

"Not a lot is expected."

I have often played with this ideology of zero expectation bringing happiness and fulfilment. It's a work in progress with a negative outcome so far. I am not yet convinced by having zero expectations. I get the concept; I understand it in principle, but I feel a sense of abandonment to those I love. Holding zero expectation is, to me, like releasing hope into the air. Hope is all we ever have. It is the ground upon which we build our dreams upon.

Does having zero expectation of self and others liberate or hinder? Is this the answer that you and I have been seeking in the search for love? Could love be the liberation and freedom of zero expectations?

2. FAMILY'S EXPECTATIONS

This next revelation made me gasp. How unalike the expectations that our sons and daughters deposit upon us are. More to the point, do we expect them to be different, due to their gender?

"Depends on the relationship, mother to daughter relationship high expectation; mother to son less expectation."

Then a twist appeared, out of nowhere. One woman expressed the self-expectation of being a good daughter in order to be a good person. She believed that the men in her life expected it too. Even her mother expected her to do everything.

This was getting too complicated. I hate to say it, perhaps the responsibility of expectation lies with just one. It is "self" that generates the burden of expectation, not others. Others merely follow the pattern that we ourselves have drawn.

Then a teacher appeared from within. Her answer to this question stopped me in my tracks.

"I have shed the role of expectation."

My follow-up question, as always, was: "How do I do that?" I have yet to find the practical cure to the shedding process.

Only one woman spontaneously mentioned self-expectation as a strain.

"I have a high expectation of self. Everything is on me."

Hoorah for the next woman who brought optimism into the arena. It was beginning to feel like a bloodbath of battered gladiators.

"I expect to be consistent in my business life, to be positive and motivated."

Thank goodness this one woman stood tall. I was only seeing the weight and burden dumped upon each woman. I was not seeing the trueness and meaning of expectation.

Historically, within the meaning of the word "expectation", was hope and an excited anticipation.

To hold an expectation of another, trust and reliability were the two companions needed.

I love being the one everyone can count on. Do you feel the same? When all the chips are down, we rise to the hopes and needs of others.

Bird's reflection upon the findings

Expectations can create a block that can stop you from allowing yourself to love and be loved. Just look at the weight unconditional love carries. It is expected of us mothers to love our children unconditionally. That in itself creates a wall, sometimes too high to even attempt, let alone to get over. To love our partners with the contracted vows of "for better, for worse". So, I am expected to love you, regardless, no matter what? The greater the expectation, the higher the failure risk.

No wonder, expectation has the potential to strip the goodness from your beloved.

But it's more complicated than expectation being a ball and chain dragged by each woman to every relationship, a deadweight of "never being good enough".

Expectation blackmails your self-worth because when you get lost in expectation, you lose sight of who you are and, more to the point, who you are becoming.

I was confused during each interview as to why expectation did not come with any optimism in all but one woman. Expectation is a two-way energy in every relationship. From one to the other and back again. It is a sharing, an absorption of faith and certainty, that I have got you and you have got me. If I must hold expectations, this is the kind I want to hold.

I know I need to listen and hear more before I come to a decision on whether love is having or giving no expectation of self or others. It seems unthinkable to me, when you work so hard for success or growth, to have zero expectation of self or others. Yet again, something so simple and the most difficult to put into practice could be the answer.

Question 11

"What does a strong woman look like to you?"

"REAL: SOMETIMES NOT PRETTY…
IT'S EARTHY."

WOMAN NO. 9

Is this, the label "strong", an identity or a characteristic that enables you to be successful in your life? Is the word inherently positive or can it be negative too?

I asked this question because I wanted to know where we begin, as women, to become strong, powerful and certain? I know as an endurance Ironman athlete that training to become strong comes with more failure and pain than wins.

I have had so many failures, felt so much pain that I have risen and been called strong. Perhaps when they call me by this name, they are right?

However, I have taken this judgement as an insult at times, even when I know it was meant with admiration and kindness. Only on a few occasions have I felt being called "strong" to be blasphemous. It was as if they were somehow diminishing my situation "It's alright for you, you're strong". When it was not "alright for me!" I had to put in the work, the same as you. The only difference is they did not see the journey, only you see each step you take.

If I am this, then why have I not received the trophy of everlasting love? If I am so bloody strong, why did he let me go? I needed the ladies to shine bright with their answers.

The answers

Amazingly, one woman had "Never thought about it." This is common, to not see daily words laid upon us and therefore never needing to question the meaning or intent behind those words.

Only two women felt that strength was negative.

> **The female has to be the protector and provider.**

"To call a woman strong, is an insult." She explained that we are both weak and strong all in the same moment or at different points in our lives. That showing our weakness is not in isolation of strength; in fact, it is because we are strong that we can speak of our weaknesses. It is just timing that separates the two identities.

One woman said it beautifully:

"This feels emotionless, not nice really. Too judgemental. We judge ourselves to be strong, too much and others lay judgement upon us too."

However, all ten women spoke the same script. Strength is an uneven fragment of them being the woman they find themselves being at this stage of their lives. Most drew on themes of being able to stand up for themselves in some way.

Here's what "she" looks like to them.

"A woman who is prepared and willing to say it and be it, the way it is."

"Vocal, but not silent."

"To say, 'I am afraid', 'I got this', 'I don't know'."

"Doesn't look like anything to me. I suppose if I have to say, she is resilient and able to cope, no matter what."

"Stands up for themselves."

"Someone who is prepared to put their own needs first. It's not one thing."

Upon hearing the following words, the true essence of a woman advertised itself on a billboard. Far too enormous to miss.

"The beauty of being a woman is she is allowed to be weak and strong. To be quiet and strong. To be resilient and cope and fail. Protecting what is important to me."

"The female has to be the protector and provider."

What you do not hear from these words are the pauses that these women took as they thought about strength. I do not want to prescribe the sense of failure I felt from each woman, but the unspoken words, the space between, was a clear enough nod to their invisible failures. Look, you and I know those failures had to occur to create strength.

Is that where the truth lies, in the silent unspoken words? To be a strong woman you must have failed and felt the worst of pains more than you have ever had success? Is success the underdog?

As one woman said to me, "What's the alternative?"

Powerful question!

If you and I are not strong, what is the alternative?

Bird's reflection upon the findings

When I asked this question, it was for validation and understanding. Did these women, like me, sometimes feel the weight of being "a strong woman". Did they understand that this playground name-calling gave those that called me "strong" an excuse or a pass to not even try to reach their highest potential? Remember the constant phrased that was dumped upon me, "It's alright for you!"

Perhaps the real reason we label others is to mask our own vulnerability. If I put you in an elevated position that, to me, is unreachable, then I do not need to tap into a power I believe I do not or could never have to get to where you are. The sisterhood can be a cruel dynasty.

The answers showed the opposite. That most of the women found this label to be a worthy one to hold. They displayed with their words a detailed avatar of what a strong woman looked like. This is the sisterhood I want to be immersed in.

We stand as one in bewilderment as to what a strong woman is. We don't have a single clear definition or know if strength is a component necessary for being an independent woman with love surrounding her ever-changing colourful aura.

All standing to attention in a singular collective belief. How powerful to know that you are me and together we are one.

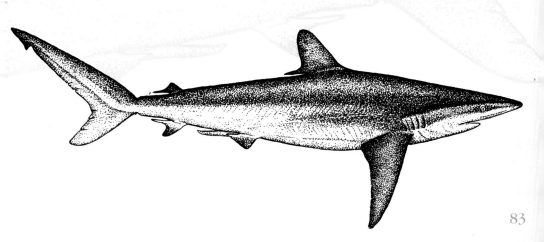

SANDBAR SHARK

Carcharhinus plumbeus

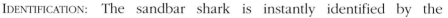

IDENTIFICATION: The sandbar shark is instantly identified by the enormous first dorsal fin.

DISTRIBUTION: Worldwide in temperate and tropical waters, including the Mediterranean.

SIZE: It may attain 3 metres, although most are around 2 metres in length.

HABITAT: The sandbar shark is a wide-ranging requiem shark that occurs both in shallow inshore and deeper offshore environments in many parts of the world.

DIET: Feeds mainly on small fishes and benthic animals.

COMMENTS: Although it is recorded from the Red Sea and it certainly ought to be seen occasionally by divers, sightings are all but unknown. Perhaps the sandbar cruises during the day at depths inaccessible to the scuba diver, as is the case in some other parts of the world. In the Red Sea it may come into shallower water at night to feed. There is film footage of sandbar sharks on the Great Barrier Reef at night, although I am not aware of daytime sightings. Or again, divers may simply not know how to identify it.

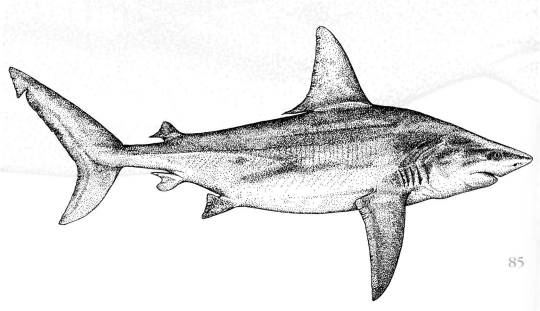

TAWNY SHARK

Nebrius concolor.

IDENTIFICATION:	The body is a uniform brown-grey colour. The eyes are tiny. There are pronounced nasal barbels. Although there are five gill slits, the proximity of the fourth to the fifth makes it appear that there are only four. The origin of the first dorsal fin is over the pelvic fin. The second dorsal fin is almost as large as the first.
DISTRIBUTION:	In warm waters from the Red Sea and East African coast to occasional island groups in the Central Pacific.
SIZE:	Attains over 3 metres in length.
HABITAT:	A bottom-dwelling shark of coral reefs. Being nocturnal it usually spends the day hidden in caves or under coral ledges.
DIET:	It feeds mainly on crustaceans such as the spiny lobster and crabs, as well as octopuses. No doubt the tawny shark also ingests any suitable bony fish it finds asleep.
COMMENTS:	The tawny shark is a placid animal that poses little threat to divers unless molested.

PELAGIC THRESHER SHARK
Alopias pelagicus

IDENTIFICATION: The pelagic thresher is instantly identified by the enormous upper lobe of the tail. The only other shark with such a long tail is the variegated shark, whose body is marked with dark spots. Furthermore the pelagic thresher is typically encountered swimming off deep-water reefs while the variegated shark is usually at rest on the sand in shallow water.

DISTRIBUTION: Recorded from many tropical and subtropical locations throughout the Indo-Pacific.

SIZE: Maximum size is probably less than 4 metres.

HABITAT: The pelagic thresher is an open-water shark that is frequently seen at depths greater than about 20 metres on offshore Red Sea reefs. It is also occasionally seen off coastal reefs.

DIET: Thresher sharks, of which this is the only species recorded from the Red Sea, use the immensely elongated upper lobe of the tail as a weapon to strike and stun fishes and squids which are then ingested.

COMMENTS: The regularity with which divers see this shark at offshore Egyptian reefs is surprising given the rarity of thresher shark sightings from reefs in other parts of the world. I have seen a pelagic thresher swimming over the sandy promontory on the southern end of Daedalus Reef, apparently hunting in the sand – hardly the behaviour expected of an open water shark that is meant to feed exclusively by stunning free-swimming creatures with its tail.

A&A Ferrari Innerspace Visions

SCALLOPED HAMMERHEAD SHARK
Sphyrna lewini

IDENTIFICATION: There are two species of hammerhead recorded from the Red Sea: the scalloped hammerhead and the great hammerhead. The scalloped hammerhead is very frequently observed on deep dives, sometimes singly, sometimes in groups or even schools of many dozens of individuals. The great hammerhead is very rarely encountered – any hammerhead sighted is almost certainly the scalloped. The forward edge of the scalloped hammerhead's head is scalloped with five pronounced indentations. The first and second dorsal fins are not especially high. The body is golden bronze, although it looks grey at depth.

DISTRIBUTION: Probably the most abundant hammerhead. Found in tropical to warm-temperate waters worldwide, although it has not been established whether it occurs in the Mediterranean.

SIZE: Maximum size is about 4 metres but most of those seen are between 2 and 3 metres.

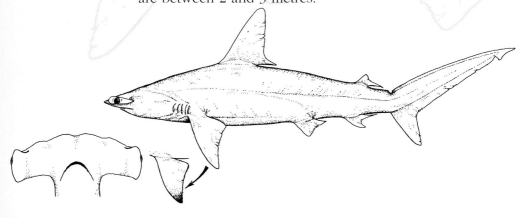

HABITAT: Apparently capable of long range migrations through open water, the scalloped hammerhead is typically seen by divers off deep-water reefs.

DIET: Feeds on a wide range of bony fishes and also small sharks. It is also capable of locating buried fishes hidden in sand and may well enter lagoon areas at night to feed on such creatures.

COMMENTS: The scalloped hammerhead seems to prefer cooler water and is usually encountered at depth (below the thermocline in summer months off Sudanese reefs). Schooling scalloped hammerheads are usually seen in the early morning (although schools have been seen later in the day) and tend to be out in the current off a promontory on the reef. While larger (solitary?) scalloped hammerheads may be dangerous, the majority are timid and difficult to approach.

GREAT HAMMERHEAD SHARK
Sphyrna mokarran

IDENTIFICATION:	The fin and head shapes are quite different from those of the scalloped hammerhead. The first dorsal fin of the great hammerhead is enormous and sickle-shaped. It comes to a thin apex and curves back markedly at its tip. The second dorsal fin is large – that of the scalloped hammerhead is much smaller. The pelvic and anal fins of the great hammerhead are also relatively large; the pelvic fins have a pronounced concave curve to the rear edge. The body is grey. The head is rectangular with a pronounced central indentation.
DISTRIBUTION:	Pan-oceanic in tropical and warm temperate waters. Rare in the Mediterranean.
SIZE:	The great hammerhead grows to considerable size – perhaps well over 6 metres.
HABITAT:	From shallow inshore waters to the open sea. It appears on both coastal and offshore reefs, although it is nowhere common.

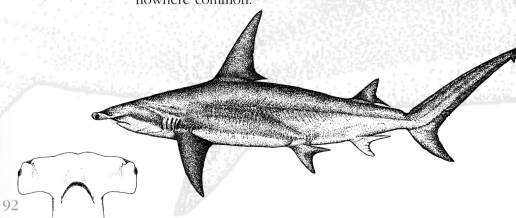

Question 12

"What does a weak woman look like?"

"IT'S HOW LONG YOU CHOOSE TO STAY."

WOMAN NO. 3

The opposite of the last question takes us deeper into the degradation of woman. My sincere apologies. I always honour every woman, even when being shown the worst side of her. Sometimes I wonder why I have my thoughts. I know they could come across as damning. It is the curse of being a truthteller.

Do we need to know what weakness looks like to know and see strength? Is it a binary thing or a spectrum, can we be sometimes strong and sometimes weak?

> **Returning to abuse, that's weak. I have done that all my life.**

Can we have moments of weakness and remain strong? I hoped that the words of others could help me (and you) find a way through the slurry of our self-loathing.

The answers

The answers were largely about two things.

1. *Loss of power*

2. *Inaction*

1. LOSS OF POWER

The first answer opened my eyes with diamond clarity.

"A woman out of her power, lost and alone."

I have been this woman. I have chosen to stay playing at being this woman. Not for long, but long enough. I have chosen to leave this woman as myself. I have chosen to leave my friends when being this woman.

Being "this woman" always leads me into the script of a victim. The unjustness of life, the "why me!" and the "it's not fair." That is who I chose to leave, the woman who believes the attention given from self and friends is applause. It never is, it's disguised. Time will show the audience who you choose to be.

"It's when we ignore these moments, we are weak." We reach our "Had Enough Moment".

Isn't it hilarious when a wise woman quotes back to you your very own words? Or maybe it takes another woman to remind you of your own wisdom.

2. INACTION

Not acting in your best interests was a theme that came up over and over again.

"Self-sabotaging with addictions, eating, drinking, putting on weight… That's weakness."

"Not happy with the things in their lives. They whinge about it and continue to do nothing to change it."

Powerful words. Our tolerance levels as other supportive women to our woman council seem to have a timescale. The time you choose to stay there, and whether you return and how often appears to be the judge and jury.

"Weak women stay, in fear, and do nothing."

"Returning to abuse, that's weak. I have done that all my life."

Interestingly, even though the judgement falls upon other women for being and doing this, you and I have been there and done that too.

The active involvement in judgment was deemed weakness. In fact, the exact words were "massive judgement". As if it needed a clarity of size. Isn't judgment grand enough?

Bird's reflection upon the findings

We have all been addicted to staying in some state or other that was no good for us: "eating, drinking, putting on weight."

We have all stayed in abuse: not wanting the marriage/relationship to end, regardless of the merit of the reason.

We have all self-sabotaged and returned to the crime scene. The seduction of being wanted.

"We are all weak."

"Weak and strong at the same time."

You are not alone in your judgement, in your name-calling and in your ignorance of self and others. Or should I replace "you" with 'I'?

I have been all but choose to never return to this state of being. Take my hand, come with me.

Question 13

"What's the opposite of a strong woman?"

"UNINSPIRING, CONTINUES TO WHINGE AND
HAVE THE WILL TO CHANGE BUT DOESN'T.
FRIENDS CAN'T KEEP LISTENING."

WOMAN NO. 2

You might think this question is the same as the last one, just the other way around. However, this is different. Is the opposite of a strong woman a weak woman? Not necessarily. I wanted to open the pathway as part of the process of discovery. Is there a spectrum? Or would it be as binary as strong opposing weak?

This question was asked for one other important reason: to not lead the witness! I did not want to lead the interview in any way. Remember, I did not necessarily ask the questions in order. I followed the words of each woman, the flow was guided by her, not I.

I lead the interviews hoping that each question would peel back the layers of emotional complexities. To get rid of what people say as being the right thing, or the thing that people think I want to hear. So, instead, they tell me their truths, regardless of what I may think of them.

Sing like a canary, ladies… No matter what words you say or with which tone.

The answers

As with the question about weakness, lack of action was apparent in some of the answers.

Sometimes the words I write on the page are cold from the lips of the experienced woman. The woman who has lived life and sometimes struggled, the woman who goes onto judge others for being who they are, only to return home confused as to why she has behaved in such a manner. This confusion is a strength in itself.

Even though the words from these women come across cold, they are full of wanting to understand and compassion.

"

Time will allow
the strong
woman to rise.

"

Even though a woman is weak, "Maybe inside they are doing all they can do?"

I thoughtfully apply this to my own relationships. Whoever they are with, maybe the other person is doing their best? Their circumstances may be different to mine and, likewise, their emotional intelligence.

Here's the compassion for another woman.

"Just a woman staring in front of another woman."

"A softer side to being strong. A more nurturing, less protective nature."

I loved this woman when she exclaimed: "There is not an opposite, there is just a woman."

Many times, in each of these interviews, I was brought to tears. This was one of the moments when teardrops melted away the ink on the page. All the answers showed me that there is no opposite. Just another opinion of what strong is perceived to be.

Bird's reflection upon the findings

These women's brutal truth forged an idea within me. Could it be that the opposite of strength is not weakness but the absence of feeling strong?

Forgive my prudence, I so want to champion

and honour women for all that they can give in each moment. BUT sometimes, just breathing, just holding a space with you is all she has to give. I remember my ex-husband leaving me five days after having our third baby. He absconded with the next-door neighbour. (I know, lazy, right?) How would you have judged my behaviour? Because some days, breathing was too much to bear.

I was on my torn, bloodied knees. I begged for the strength just to take the next breath. Have you ever been in such grief where you are drowning in sorrow? Sorrow crushes your chest with the heavy regret that you must take the next breath, not for yourself but for the little prisoners that have been sentenced along with you to a life not wanted.

I wanted someone, anyone, to come and take my babies away so that they would be free from my despair. Was I weak for feeling and thinking these disgraceful unmotherly thoughts? Or was I strong for actioning each laborious, loathing breath? And then after that breath, I took another, then another, until I formed a willingness to maybe breathe for the next hour. The hours turned into days and time passed the baton of responsibility over to me to forge my way back into wanting to live an extraordinary life.

What if being strong is the moment of just being, not taking action but looking to be strong?

Sit, my darling.

Breath.

Aspire to be strong.

Look up…

Do the daily work to figure out what is the next best move for you.

YOU.

Time will allow the strong woman to rise.

Question 14

"What is important to you now?"

"GIVING AWAY LOVE WITH
NO RETURN."

WOMAN NO. 5

If you have listened to the words spoken from the most extraordinary guests that I have had the honour to interview on my radio show, you would know that I like to dive deep into the reasons why people do what they do. Not one of my guests has ever said that money, fame or notoriety was the reason they do what they do. Yes, it was the primary motivator and side effect but never the underlying reason. NEVER! Family was the

"

We are
hardwired to
find love.

"

only reason each person sacrificed, compromised and suffered in their work or business lives.

Family.

If that's not true love, I don't know what is.

I was curious to see how important that which I sought (love) was to these women, or perhaps something else might be more important in this fifth decade of their life.

The answers

It seems I am not the only one who believes in love but – perhaps not surprising at this age – health also proved to be very important. Not just their own health but the health of their loved ones too.

1. *Love*

2. *Health*

1. LOVE

"Above all, it is most important to love and be loved."

"We are hardwired to find love."

Do you ever sometimes think it is just you who is weird and wonderous in your thoughts? When I heard this woman's words, it was like she said my most secret thoughts aloud. In fact, I found myself inwardly chanting to myself "told you so". "I knew it" was never far from falling off my lips.

In this decade, women may retire, their children may leave home (albeit with the action of a boomerang. They come and go, not permanently leaving, YET!) and sometimes women suffer the loss of parents or close family relatives, so the love of friends becomes more important than ever.

"The people around me are the people I serve now. This has become more important than ever."

"My family and friends are the most important things to me."

"As my parents have died, my extended family and dear friends have become more important to me."

The loss of dear ones has violently altered these women's perceptions of what is important. The speed of change can be aggressive. It shapes a new love in friendships. They emerge from the once murky waters of a busy family life – one clouded by the importance of work, of children's messy needs and an absent, hard-working partner.

When you strip away your day and the people in it, what is left of importance to you?

2. HEALTH

These women in their fiftieth decade all wanted this one word for themselves and others. Remember this is something that mattered more now than when they were younger. It was the most heavily repeated word when answering this question. I found it hard to believe, as this has definitely not been shown to me in people's behaviours, actions or bodies.

"Health."

"Health and the family's health matters now, we have nothing else."

Was it that perhaps suffering illness or disease had brought health to the forefront? Health is an anomaly; it only becomes important when it is stolen from us too early in life. Surely, health should've mattered then as it matters now. Or is that just me?

Bird's reflection upon the findings

Very rarely do I regret or wish to go back to my past wrongs and put them right. Yet, I cannot help but feel that so much that matters now, could have been put in place back then, years ago. It is never too early for healthy living and investing in self-worth.

Yet this is a fallacy, for if I wind the clock back, I know that what matters now never mattered back then. It couldn't have. Life had not happened yet. There is an ever-changing continuum of importance throughout our lives, which is only present in that moment. This fifties decade is my decade. I honour the experiences of love felt and lost, the delicious taste of devotion and the sourness of rejection. Through this passage of time, healing is at the forefront of growth and actioning wisdom is the pinnacle of daily living.

Question 15

"Is it easier to stay or leave?"

"BIG BREATH… MONEY CRAVES
THE DECISION."

WOMAN NO. 6

To say I am always pondering this question is an understatement. For me, this question had to be asked. I question the judgements I have made regarding whether to stay or leave relationships whether that be a with partner, friend, family member or even a job. It's always a big decision, and do we ever really know if we've made the right one?

Why did I choose to leave, and you chose to stay? This question haunts me. Truly.

Could this one deed of leaving be the reason for not having a lifelong partner of love?

Living history together is lost once you leave. Just like the dinosaurs. Only you know the shared stories of the past. Those histories have little or no relevance to the life you share today. The historical heroes (or loves) of our lives become mere stories to the loving ears of your tenderly chosen present partner. The living ghosts have no visible presence to your partner of today, they are mere stories you share to help him understand how life has shaped you.

Perhaps the question I ask myself the most is whether leaving the immediate pain cut me off from the potential rewards of an endured relationship. As you and I know, pain always ends; it's not will it end, it's when. How long do we take the pain, how much can one person tolerate until you reach your "had enough" moment?

I have never made sense of this innate dilemma. Time has not soothed the internal dialogue nor doubt. I hoped that these sages of sisterhood may just be my wise saviours. I needed to know…

The answers

As with all humungous questions, the answer is never binary, especially when it's asked to women. We are complex beings, thank goodness. I love us for it. But I sometimes just want to hear masculine simplicity in the answer.

Teleport yourself back to the interviews with me and each woman. Watch how their emotional intellect places them in a cosy sub-group within an already micro-intimate group. Truly phenomenal.

Out of the ten women, two camps appeared. The split was seventy/thirty. Seventy per cent of the women interviewed said it was easier to stay and thirty per cent said easier to leave.

1. *Stay*

2. *Leave*

1. STAY

Horror, I thought the sages would've agreed with my action to leave. I wanted to walk out at this precise moment of terror.

Two revelations surfaced from our tearful words. The tears were from both sides of the conversation.

You are the owner of your worth.

"Staying can go one of two ways."

"Staying is less intense, but it drips away at you. The leaving is intense, but the pain goes away fast."

Be seated with me and their murderous words and see the formidable women appear. Show yourself the courage to stay on these pages and hear the traumatic truth of love.

"It's easier to stay for everybody else. Do not cause the mayhem. You find a place you just accept and now it is easier... (cavernous pause)... I have a nice life."

I cannot tell you how hearing her torturous words closed my throat over. I felt hands in the air squeezing my throat a little too hard. Was it to silence my beliefs of what I deemed was the wrong decision, or was it to silence her doubt and regret of her right decision?

But I heard and felt her powerful words. I bowed to the decisions she had the courage to make. There is true beauty in a courageous woman. Making a decision with no idea of the lifelong consequence or outcome. Just the knowledge that it has to be made and lived through.

"One decision is made, that is it."

I love this next reason to stay. It always makes me chuckle. Definitely not from a woman in her twenties.

"Easier to stay, nobody else would put up with my crap."

I hate the word "crap'" and I hate to hear the desertion of self. To this lady, I wanted to whisper, "keep reaching." Don't you dare dispense of yourself. You are not that trodden, soggy teddy bear that a spoilt child no longer wants because they deem it time for a new one. You do not need a new owner to see your worth. You are the owner of your worth.

This is only the fifth decade; I cannot allow these fifty-something-year-old sages to steal my dreams of growing into my greatness as the number of my years gets bigger.

And breathe!

More of the women agree: "The relationship is quite handy; I have no desire to leave."

"Stay regardless."

I wanted to stay, I truly did. I believe in the sanctity of marriage as much now as I did then, and in the enduring love of forever togetherness. But I couldn't stay and lose the higher love. A love of one's own.

My admiration for the self-sacrifice of these women is overwhelming. I am confused about who nurtures their blindness. Is it self-inflicted or does the environment manipulate the scene?

Am I blind to the riches you endure or are you closing your eyes tight to the liberation of being loved by only one, yourself? This is a question for all the sisterhood. You, me and all the women who are awakening.

Just sit with that before moving on. Don't rush away from these words. They are not meant to torment you, merely to tickle your self-told stories.

2. LEAVE

Then there are the leavers.

"Always leave."

You have to admit, it is wonderful to see black and white in the polemic mist, whatever the outcome is.

"It's hard to leave, much harder, but easier in the long run. You come through the transition quicker."

"Leaving takes strength. It takes a lot of strength."

Then a woman walks into her words after saying she had left a relationship and dropped the mic.

"It is helpful if you are financially independent. Money provides you with choice. Money craves a decision and once the decision is made. That is it."

Bird's reflection upon the findings

It is not the answer that will save me, but the peace I will find when releasing the righteousness to the question. In other words, regardless of what your decision is, you should make the decision and leave it there. Life is cleverer than you and I, we will never know what the right answer was. That's the beauty of life. Do not question the rightness of it. It is made, move on.

As a habitual, inquisitive problem-solver, my struggle with these women's answers remains. Knowing and doing are worlds apart. For me, it's like being a polar bear in the Sahara Desert. Unthinkable, it hurts my brain, my eyesight goes all fuzzy just thinking about it. If we never know if we were right, how can we survive, let alone learn from our decisions, adapt and grow?

I don't know how to do the "letting go" shit! How do I do that? Again, spare me your words of theory and share with me your tips of practicality.

Letting go is a theory, looking forward, not looking back, is a practicality.

I can do that.

You can do that.

Be blinded to the past and see the future. It is oh so bright, my darling.

Question 16

"Are you at the end of who you are to become, and if not, can you change your personality?"

"SUPPRESS OR ELEVATE."

WOMAN NO. 10

I sense the fifth decade is a vast decade of self-permission. It is one of acceptance and, as is sung in *The Greatest Showman*, "This is me." (I dare you not to sing it!)

Which leads me onto asking: if I am accepting and happy with who I am, do I need to keep growing, learning or evolving? These actions are always so painful and expensive, with time as the loan shark.

For a woman who likes to challenge herself, grow, and be ridiculously successful, the work feels like it is never done. Whatever I am doing is never enough, and I am left awake at night always wanting more. Are you?

But am I just putting too much pressure on myself? Don't just tell me, ladies, show me.

The answers

You will notice the shortness of these answers. Succinct and directly to the point. Each woman created a certainty for me. I trusted them immediately. I believed every word and respected their beliefs, whatever they were.

Each woman, no matter what life cocktail they had drunk, brought an air of acceptance to their words. I breathed these majestic women in.

One woman out of ten said, "No, I am who I am."

One woman out of the ten elaborated, "This is who I am today, always learning."

What said the other ladies?

"Am I the person I was when I was married? No. You grow, you grow into knowledge, insights, experiences." She

> **You grow into knowledge, insights, experiences.**

stops for a massive pause in her speech, and then follows this with, "Feelings change." Her words virtually stared at me with certainty.

Again, she appeared from the flames, the woman I have been seeking. Certain and true. Regardless, no matter what.

I am learning that I don't need to agree with your choices because your conviction brings me a welcoming nod of truth. I feel safe with you, that's the power of being this woman.

"Now I have a healthy regard for my personality. All the light and darkness of it brings me to who I am today."

A self-truth decision-making machine appears from underneath the silk cloth, like a long-awaited piece of art being unveiled to the public for the first time.

Bird's reflection upon the findings

Time promotes acceptance. It seems the clock ticking provides you with all you have been seeking, the art of NGAF (Not Giving A Fuck). I hate swearing, apologies.

When my big people were little, I refused to swear in front of them and created a language, changing the sounds of the real words to those of rhyming words. Instead of saying, "Fuck it," I would say, "Two peas in a bucket." Genius, right? Still hate them swearing now, the buggers.

Few women agreed on the changeability of their personality or becoming the woman they were meant to be. Some said with conviction a simple, short "NO" and some laughed, answering YES, of course, silly.

What all of the women agreed on – interestingly, blaming their age and being in their fifties – was that they now didn't care what people thought of anything. They couldn't care less what people thought of them. Whether their opinions were agreed with, what they looked like or what choices they made in their lives. Nada!

Success, work harder, work more efficiently, be more, have more was a myth. You cannot be more, work harder and show success if you are held back by what people think. That was the growth lesson, the metamorphosis into accomplished, triumphant carefree women.

Be carefree.

Be more.

Be you.

Question 17

"Do you have more compassion now?"

"I UNDERSTAND PEOPLE."

WOMAN NO. 4

We women can be the meanest of the bunch. We want to rise and grow, but I am yet to find the sisterhood who want to rise together. Brutal words, but true for me. I know some of you have found your women, your sisterhood. I love that. I wait with a smile.

Confidence (or lack of), judgement and inaction are the root cause of our venom. We have been dragging around our lack of self-compassion and acceptance with us through the decades, like a scented rag being pursued by the hounds on a mock fox hunt.

I wanted to ask this question because, in my own life, I have supported and judged, and have shown plentiful compassion (and none) for both myself and my fellow sisters. Am I lacking in compassion, even when I believe I have bountifully given love? Why have I found that vital in my search for love?

The answers

Compassion seems to fall into 2 camps:

3. *Compassion for self*
4. *Compassion for others*

1. COMPASSION FOR SELF

Each woman shared that she'd had minimal compassion for herself and others in her twenties and yet now finds herself abundant in the will to self-accept and even, dare I say it, "like" themselves. Seeing the world in a less competitive way in her fifties has created a less threatening atmosphere with others.

"Yes, I do, I have the ability to give to someone else without the expectation of anything. I have always been compassionate for others, that's easy, but not for self."

Compassion was largely answered in a very indirect

and unfamiliar sense to self. Then this truth slipped gently out of the mouth of a lioness.

"Most of my friends have had one or another level of infidelity, most don't leave. My compassion for myself and them has grown exponentially."

Every syllable gripped me as I hung on to hear the next sound she uttered. I only saw and understood the sentence standing back from the billboard of her words. This is the art of compassion in progress. You are who I want in my sisterhood.

I nodded in agreement. Knowing that each woman in her pain of infidelity needs more compassion from all that surrounds her than ever before. The compassion of silence, to not say one word, to sit with zero judgment of the outcome and to accept her decision with love. That level of compassion has only ever mattered now, in this moment. It most certainly didn't matter back then, when time was a friend, not a judge awarding a life sentence.

2. COMPASSION FOR OTHERS

This was "simple, stupid."

"Yes, I'm less judgemental now because of the confidence and acceptance I have found in ageing."

> **"** I'm less judgemental now because of the confidence and acceptance I have found in ageing. **"**

"My capacity for compassion is greater now."

"My capacity for compassion builds."

"Yes, I do, to give to someone else without the result of anything. I have always been compassionate for others. That's easy, but not for self."

Clearly, every woman found compassion a breeze and gifted it readily to one another. Each woman was more shocked at me for asking the question. Being compassionate was comparable to breathing; for them, it's unconscious, involuntary and you have no choice in this action. You just are.

Bird's reflection upon the findings

I have no idea what you believe the ageing process looks and feels like. But these women, throughout all their experiences, have learned to truly understand people. In this realisation, compassion has grown exponentially. Mirroring to self with every sisterhood relationship.

Do we, in this decade, practice compassion in its truest meaning "to co-suffer"? Unequivocally, yes.

Question 18

"What do you understand today because of what happened yesterday?"

"DON'T LOOK BACK."

WOMAN NO. 1

By the time you have entered your fifth decade, would it be true to say that a fair amount of suffering has been gifted upon you and me? It's likely you have been through some tough times. Some less than others.

Some of us consciously choose calamity to gain our desired outcome, others fall into misfortune with their eyes wide shut.

Should you and I look back in order to understand,

"

Don't look back.

"

take action on our past, go to counselling, and seek support to discuss the antiquated demeanour once undertaken by ourselves or others? Should we go deep into the past to find the answers in our history or "Just keep swimming"... Thank you, Disney's *Finding Nemo*.

I wanted to know whether delving into the history of our lives, putting meaning where once stood self-regret, would eliminate the well-versed practice of 'history repeating itself'.

Do we need pain and suffering to learn? What could I learn from these women's yesteryears of sophistication and faux pas?

The answers

When one woman militantly spoke the words, "Don't look back," I understood. Why put yourself into the doubt of the past. Leave it there. Nothing good comes from questioning the righteousness of who we once were.

She continued, "Women tend to look at the bigger picture and make decisions from that point."

If you knew her whole story, you would wholeheartedly agree with this answer. But in isolation, it is meaningless and creates a frown of doubt upon your face. Is it doubt about whether women can make decisions? Come on, you and I know most women can be shocking at making decisions. Apologies for the provocative, generalised statement but it's true. Brutal but true.

I agree, women are amazing creatures at seeing so much more of the life picture than the single, blinkered picture sometimes focussed on by other species, men.

Every one of the women mentioned how their intention, their best intention, showed them the way. The intention always decrees the message.

"Everything is because of past experiences. I believe you are doing the best you can. I am less pissed off now and take full responsibility."

Gifting responsibility to our young women following us would inject a confidence that only history lays upon this fifty decade. Teaching responsibility as a strength rather than using blame as a resolve would raise our women to be incredible decision-makers. Responding, not knee-jerk reacting to life.

"We are all muddling through, all trying our best but may not have figured it out yet."

Are we supposed to have it all figured out in this

decade? Are we still learning as we go?

"Awareness creeps up over the decades, this allows compassion for my past."

The obviousness of the impact that the past has had on who these women have found themselves to be today was not so much evident in their words but their tone. Their tone told their story equally as their words did.

Remember, my listening was heightened due to only focussing on their words and their voice. I purposefully didn't want to see them, knowing the distraction of reading body language would disable my pure sense of hearing and skew my findings.

The marriage of tone and words gave me a deep insight into their greater ability to see their self-potential now. They were compassionate about the experiences of the past, the right and wrong of how they behaved, and the devotion given to an unconscious, largely unappreciative family. The family have no idea what women give to "the bigger picture". Neither should they. Perhaps this is a reason that these women are still seeking the courage to action a very-much-needed guiltfree single-mindedness. This is a characteristic their past experiences have inspirited them to finally practice.

Bird's reflection upon the findings

Each woman's answer was succinct and direct. In fact, each woman had very little to say in response to this question. Her intention was clear, their best was at the forefront of each day and their lives were not only focussed on themselves, but everyone.

They honoured their past, knowing:

"I wouldn't be me without that."

But all the women had no desire to gratify their past lives with words of regret or undoing.

For me, every cell in my body holds the stories of my past, but my responsible actions hold my arms out wide, preparing me for my long-awaited flight.

Question 19

_____

"What have you learnt from love?"

"LOVE, BLOOD, SWEAT AND TEARS."

WOMAN NO. 10

Here we go, let the games begin.

When I asked this out of sequence question, it got an overwhelmingly eclectic sound. The equal sound of cynicism and astuteness through their tight-lipped trophy smiles.

Was love a lesson taught by role models and peers? Or did the lessons have to come only from experience – the high and lows of loving and being loved in return. Do you learn to love from your scars or by what has been shown to be possible? Was my role modelling to

> **"** Love brings colours, yellow, bright colours like a rainbow. **"**

my daughter, Noos, going to be proven pointless or was it going to be the most wonderous movie for her to witness. Did love have to be one's own journey to feel one's own way through? Did you have to make your own mistakes and learn from them, or could you see and measure it as a bystander?

Would the women's voices and experiences be similar to my love battles or is love a currency that takes on a different form for different people?

The answers

The answers came as one-liners, simple intimate quotes. They do not fit into a trend or category. They reside alone, together.

Although the only one true trend that presented itself from these women's words was that there was no single thing they all agreed on. Each woman brought her own story of how she loved and grew into changing love through experiencing its many colours.

"Love brings colours, yellow, bright colours like a rainbow."

I adore this quote from one of the women, "Love is lovely, to be connected to someone." Reading it now, makes me smile. These words were visceral, I felt them deep in my heart.

The visual lessons appeared.

"I had clear ways of what love looked like. This came from the unconditional love of my parents."

Learning to love again was a message that came through again and again.

"Learning to love me first."

"Learning to love him again (there was a time when I didn't)." At least a minute passed in silence before she could follow up with, "He's a good man".

Sit with me and breath in this woman's love experience. No judgment, just see and feel her.

"Love comes naturally, for the man that he is."

"There will be a time when the person you say it to is not there anymore."

Time is present in all these women's words. The true acknowledgement of time. Time as a commodity of duration in the relationship brought a different love.

"Love for the past twenty years has brought a comfortable love. No more sex outside."

Age seems to be answerable to how good a woman loves, that she is better at loving in her fifty decade than in her twenties.

"I was rubbish at it in my twenties."

Let's see whether the twenty decade echoes and agrees.

Who knew there were types of love?

Sacrificial Love: "Love is to sacrifice your own needs for the wants of others."

Child love: "So many types of love, love for my children is different to love for my grandchildren."

True love: "I found true love because I didn't put up with just anyone."

The many lessons learnt are truly yours to acknowledge and accept. I can merely look on in admiration of these women's truths.

Bird's reflection upon the findings

There is a scene in the movie *Love Actually* in which a character declares his secretive, forbidden love. As he walks away, he says:

"Enough (long pause), enough now." He whispers it ever so gently and ever so lovingly to himself.

I have repeatedly recoiled and thoughtfully rehearsed these words time and time again when no more can be salvaged. Love has hurt and scarred my body but taught me the power of knowing "enough", enough now. I will not and cannot take any more pain.

Be kind and gentle to yourself, my darling. Know the place from where it is coming from and that you are the love to be given from and given to.

Love comes with our own historical conditions.

Love is all we are truly seeking, sometimes beginning in the wrong place.

Love teaches us to dignify time.

Your time.

A lifetime.

Question 20

———.

"How have you practically stayed in love?"

"I IGNORE BAD BEHAVIOUR.
NO GRUDGES. NO SULK."

WOMAN NO.1

I have never been or wish to be a theorist. I do not want to tell you how to do something, I want to show you that you can.

This question always found itself being asked in the last third of each women's interview. Knowing this, you can imagine them sitting alone, chattering in isolation in the swing of sharing, of not filtering their words, and the overfloweth of truth.

" Never give up on them, whatever. "

I use these words all the time: "Show me, don't tell me."

Shine bright now ladies, the "how to tools" upon my seeking pathway. I want to know how you have practically stayed in love with your partner. Is being in love and staying in love different or is it part of the love expedition?

Surely it is not as challengingly simple as "ignore bad behaviour".

I nearly dropped to the floor from my chair when one Woman said, "Ignore bad behaviour. No grudges. No sulks."

It has to be over twenty years ago; I heard these exact words on a BBC Radio Four show topically talking about relationships. An infamous scholar shared her thoughts on the ability to create a long-life partner. "Treat men as if they were your child. Ignore the bad and reward the good." If you can have reverse misogyny, it was right there in that moment.

The answers

Again, the trends show themselves in two defined categories.

1. *Me or Him*

2. *Them (others)*

1. ME OR HIM

"Never give up on them, whatever."

BOOM... Straight into the practicality of love.

"Never", "No" and "Now" were spoken within a communal secret script. Some women couldn't help themselves but say what was on their lips, others chose to silence their courageous hidden words. Too distasteful to release. If the words are spoken aloud, then the unnerving skill of manifestation jiggles them about and "hey presto!", the words become true. Keeping silent will push the belief where it can't be reached, or that's the wish.

There is a part of me that absolutely understands and believes in manifesting our wants and desires.

Do I believe in keeping silent so that the negative thoughts, destructive unwanted thoughts don't become real? NO, I do not believe that.

I do believe in repetition, and the more you focus and speak ill of something, the more it forges a pathway of behaviour that adapts the thoughts into actions or behaviour you may not even be aware of.

What I truly know is the point of convergence. Drawing your attention to your deep wants; blinkered, undistracted focus and unmeasurable hard work are the ingredients in creating a manifesting potion.

What has become obvious in the trends of this fiftieth decade is the control you and I have on "self" and the control we voluntarily donate to "others".

The "Self-love" trend, "love you first." Very topical at this highly-charged moment in the world of women's empowerment.

"Do what feels right."

"I don't do conflict anymore. I must feel safe."

"Treat them how you expect to be treated. Return love back."

Whenever you put practice to the test, failure follows more than success. Success only comes intermittently and usually at the end of the process. So, when I heard a woman say to me, "At times it has been deadly rocky, we have hated each other at times." I followed with how? "How did you make it through, how did find love again?"

She replied, "If I wanted to stay in love with him, I had to return love back before receiving it myself."

NOOOOOOOOOOOOOOOOO!!!!!!!!! That is not

the practical tip I was hoping to hear.

It is sky blue pink clear that this is hard, so hard. It makes me feel sick to know that to be and stay in love you literally must do whatever the relationship asks of you. In other words, do whatever it takes. Only you can define the scope of "whatever it takes".

Biggest practical tip, get ready for this: You must do the deep work on yourself. It is vital you know who you are so that when the challenges appear, the push and pulls that happen in relationships, you know, cellularly know, what "whatever it takes" will require from you.

2. THEM (OTHERS)

An alternative trend to "self" is the "others" trend, how others treat you in love.

"Being told you are loved, when you are told often enough, you start to believe it."

"Keep laughing."

"Create stories together, even when you are least expecting it."

Love is an endurance sport. Pick the right sport for you and give it all you have, more, and then some more.

Ironman training gave me a wonderous pathway to self-respect and a pathway to understanding success. Success, whatever the outcome, takes focus, unwavering faith in one's own ability and the readiness to endure whatever it takes. I endured all the external and internal elements: fatigue, doubt, speed, lack of speed, negotiation with time allocation, money and perception of what was needed to be spent, judgment. I had to push through where others would not go, to be ridiculed and carry on. I did whatever was needed to get to the start line. To begin the race. The race was not the endurance part, the training process was. Race day was merely my lap of glory.

Bird's reflection upon the findings

You climb together, you fall infrequently together. You get to the end of the climb and look back hoping you see the feat of your labour and not hear the cruelness of life's jingle "it wasn't worth it".

Love takes all you have and more, it tests your whole being and then you must endure, consistently.

Do not be a fool in reading these words with antagonism. You are a participant in the love race, it is your strength that is vital for you to even begin the race. You are the athlete, it is your duty to practice, your responsibility to build love and lead with dignity and grace.

Question 21

"Do you believe in the love of your life?"

"YES, I DO… BUT YOU CAN HAVE MORE THAN ONE."

WOMAN NO. 3

A strength that was absent from the previous twenty questions appeared now, at this eleventh hour from these women of substance. (This was never the last question to be asked, but it nearly always followed question twenty and found itself in the last third of each interview.)

These women were in their flow now, happily alone with their answers. They didn't need any acceptance from me. Each woman stood in the power of what she truly believed. Each woman was now freed from caring about what anyone else thought. They didn't feel the need to sex up their stories or cover up their truths with what they thought I wanted to hear, nor play down their pain or suffering. They were real women, relaxed, enjoying this cathartic, emotional personal experience.

This obvious, obligatory question had to be asked.

Surely, when speaking about love in the interviews, this question's answer would be at the heart of these women's reasons and excuses for their relationships. Yet, it wasn't. My presumptions of love did not match theirs.

An elephant was always in the room, facing the corner when making up the whys and wherefores of the relationship's guilty, regrettable behaviour.

Isn't this the point you and I have been waiting for? Each women's voice leading us to this crunch time. Was endured love a commodity based upon finding "The One", otherwise better known as "The Love of Your Life", or was there more to it?

Was I doomed, sentenced to living in purgatory due to losing in love? Did this mean that I had left the love of my life? Or could it mean that I had I not met him yet? (Nice twist, Bird! You're welcome.

This is where it gets messy, do your worst ladies!

> **I believe in a few during my life.**

The answers

Not one woman agreed wholeheartedly nor held the same belief as another. All ten women gave a different tilt to the question and shared an alternative emotional plea to conclude the answer.

These ten women stunned me. I thought this question would've put meat on the bones of love. Instead, the answers were lean and efficient. There was minimal fat to chew on in each conversation.

There was an anger and disbelief at my personal stupidity to ask this ridiculous question. One woman shot me down with her preposterous tone: "Don't believe in it. Romantic and fluffy."

There was humour and self-ridicule from another woman towards herself. "Yes, I have met some idiots over the years."

There were young love memoirs shared. "First boyfriend, he still makes my heart flutter now when I think of him."

There was an enlightenment to love. "A relationship that felt more than the love of my life, an intense love. God."

Three women truly loved the fact that they had a plentiful supply of "The One".

"I believe in a few during my life."

"The love of my life is now." Read into that what you will, my darling.

My preconceived ideas of this decade have been torpedoed out of the water.

I had presumed that most would've said "yes" to believing in "The One" due to being born into the dogma of the sanctity of marriage. When they were young, the belief was: one man for life, not just for Christmas.

In actual fact, many of these women, now in their fifties, did not believe in "The One" – shocking, I know! Had they forgotten what zest and dreams they held in their twenties? Are you really telling me, ladies, that even back then, one true love didn't matter? That, as a young woman, you never believed your man was your "one"? That doesn't make sense to me. Yet the beliefs of this fifty decade would show and tell otherwise.

Bird's reflection upon the findings

The history of our ancestors has moulded the way we think to show us what it takes to love. I wonder if our mothers understood the seriousness of their job of modelling our ideas of womanhood.

We take the shape of our mothers until we allow our beautiful, brave bodies to live and love openly.

It bothers me to see my belief in "The One" being dirtied by the misery of murderous failed marriages. I have had to do the work to still believe in love. I am still doing the work, isn't that the irony of love. The work is you. Building belief in your abilities, dreaming the impossible and trying, falling, and getting right back up, again and again and again.

So...oooo

Who is she, the woman in her fifties?

Here is society's description of the mysterious woman who appears in her fifth decade: an apocalyptic hormonal, empty nester tragedy. If a screenplay were to be written for this historically misunderstood character, it would go something like this:

"A woman desperately seeking her sensual, spirited self after many decades of self-loathing, body dysmorphia, low self-esteem and a cavernous confidence crisis. What a shame it's all a little too late for her. The hormones have left her baron with a desert-dry vagina and a libido that belongs to a flea, a body that won't stop leaking sweat or wee and grey roots that smell."

Ohhh, please tell me that has just made you die with laughter. And if you have identified yourself as that woman, call me!

I'm pleased to tell you that this mythical creature is not whom I discovered.

The woman I met was sassy with an air of abandonment. She was more carefree of others than ever and getting more comfortable with putting herself first.

She was finally creating an unwalled space for her new-ly-found growth, rhythmically nurturing and intermit-tently losing love in the decades that had gone before her. She was kind, full of love and compassion for her friends and family, even if she'd long since left the romanticism of youth.

So why do I feel a bit disappointed by her?

I can't believe we, women, have rallied and protest-ed for a hundred years and yet we are still in the same love coliseum. We are still fighting as invisible warriors, with an inch more of boldness to our righteous voice.

I thought we had moved far, far away from some of the words repeated through each interview.

I have a strong sense of not wanting women to accept or endure relationships that imprison them. I found it hard to hear of these women's suffering, what they have had to put up with to keep their relationship awake. I wished it wasn't so. I wished for ambition and self-fulfilment to be their lifelong companions rather than an afterthought for when the children decided they no longer required the safety of home.

But I get it. I understand why. My own impatience

creates my disappointment, not these beautiful, brave women of the fifty decade.

Rising takes time.

Rising takes courage.

Rising takes togetherness.

But here is the truth, I came here to listen and collate their wisdom on the dangers of love, to look for trends that could help me in my own life. It is not my place to judge other women's relationships, their partners or their choices in life. I unquestionably know we are all doing our best in each hour.

At first, I could only see the word "tolerate" sarcastically illuminated within the darkness. The initial evidence was proving to be what I had feared. If Noos or I were to find love again, we had to just simply shut up and tolerate. No, no and how about NO!

I refuse to role model for myself, or my daughter, the becoming of The Goddess of Toleration. Especially if what I was tolerating was actually the wrong love for me, not my "one" but one I should unregrettably leave.

With a heavy heart and a will to go deeper into the

collective trends spoken by each woman, my disappointment thawed drip by drip, my vision cleared and I saw a rich woman among the collective. A woman in her fifties with a personal wealth that took decades to build. Awake to the solutions that were right for her.

I love the women in this fifty decade

They have identified the importance of sculpting their voice, of balancing generational family expectations with self-worth. They have taught me to consciously ignore the friendly critics – one of their most precious qualities.

On the flip side, financial independence is not a quality held by most of these women. I believe it is crucial that you make your own money to put into the same pot that your partner does. It does not have to be in equal money value, but it does have to be equal in percentage and intention. That's pure equality.

The opposite of this is not building your own personal wealth or naming a secret bank account "The Just in Case Account" or the "Pocket Money Account". If something is hidden, secret or not spoken about, guilt, fear and shame become partners in crime. Empowerment, confidence and growth cannot even begin to be your focus when you are sat waiting, maybe knowing that the end is nigh. Not yet, not soon, but it's coming. Your womanly wisdom knows and without financial independence, your control of visible choices is diminished.

I wished these women had built up the freedom to choose by earning and contributing their own money. Money is the currency that boosts your ability to make decisions, it brings you to the table and empowers you to voice your beliefs.

These brilliant women are kind, caring and intentionally tolerant, always with the outcome in mind. Staying true to the path of parenting and partnering, they know when to let go and when to keep close. Having given to others constantly, they are now growing into shamelessly giving to themselves.

They know what is needed now to move into being who they were born to be: confident, sensuous and provocative.

Ladies, this decade has a duty, a responsibility to inspire the women following. To be carefree and light the sky with their abilities.

Acknowledgements

2 women and 10 to honour.

Noos…. yet again you challenge me to a duel with love, self-duty and the responsibility of being your mumma. Thank you, my cherub, for holding me up when all I want to do is lay down.

Leila… What a wonderful journey we have begun to walk together. You have the courage to be brutal with what is needed from the writing and the softness to deliver daily encouragement. Thank you, my darling, for weaving your talent as a publisher and editor, within my words.

You Beautiful Brave 10 Women standing.

How magnificent you are…

How generous you are…

How wise you are…

Thank you, your legacy is written and chiselled into my heart and the hearts of the many women who follow you.

About Beautiful
Brave Body

Beautiful Brave Body is an awe-inspiring place for women seeking empowerment and purpose to come for advice, courses, and to join a loving, truthful community of like-minded women.

It's a safe place to explore your bravery. I created an environment for women like you to see just how beautiful they are and support them to live with an abundance of energy and love.

It emerged from the architecture of my previous business, Bird on a Bike, which was forged seven years ago after losing everything and finding so much to share. It was business built upon daily rituals and fitness for women.

After many years of listening daily to women's silent voices and feeling frustrated that they would beg for support, yet not have the courage to hold my hand, something had to change, and so Beautiful Brave Body was born.

Come and visit us at:

BeautifulBraveBody.com

to

- join our community
- share your story with us
- sign up to hear when the next book in the series is published
- immerse yourself in the Facebook group
- dip your toe in the 5-week Facebook programme

Noos and I can't wait to meet you.

Onto the Sixties...

BV - #0058 - 121120 - C0 - 178/127/11 - PB - 9781913717155 - Matt Lamination